KS3 Success

Workbook

Science SATs

Levels 5-7

Brian Arnold • Hannah Kingston • Emma Poole

Contents

Biology

Chemistry

Physics

Homewok diary

TOPIC	STUDY DATE	SCORE
Cells		/29
Organ systems		/22
Nutrition and food tests		/29
The digestive system		/27
The heart		/20
Blood and circulation		/22
Movement		/25
The lungs and breathing		/21
Puberty and reproduction		/24
Drugs		/19
Fighting disease		/25
Photosynthesis		/19
Plant reproduction		/22
Carbon and nitrogen cycles		/19
Classification		/24
Variation		/21
Inheritance and genetics		/25
Food chains and webs		/18
Adaptation and competition		/24
Rocks		/26
The rock cycle		/28
Pollution		/23
States of matter		/26
Dissolving		/19
Particle theory		/24
Atoms and elements		/29
Metals		/35
Unusual elements		/21
Chemical reactions		/33
Reactivity series		/33
Displacement reactions		/36
Acids and alkalis		/33
Making salts		/29
Chemical tests		/27
Mixtures		/34
Separation techniques		/21
Compounds		/24
Naming compounds		/27
Balancing equations		/28
Speed		/26
Graphs of motion		/31
Forces		/29
Friction and terminal velocity		/26
Moments		/33
Pressure		/30
Light rays and reflection		/32
Refraction and colour		/32
Sounds		/35
Echoes and hearing		/29
Energy		/37
Using energy resources		/39
Alternative sources of energy		/35
Heat transfer		/27
Circuit components		/36
Circuits: current and voltage		/25
Magnets and electromagnets		/18
The Solar System 1		/27
The Solar System 2		/26

Once you have completed a unit, and filled in your score on the Homework Diary opposite, use this Progress Plotter to chart your success! Fill in the boxes with your score for each unit and watch your results get better and better.

	Nearly all right – Excellent work!	More than half – Good – but keep trying.	Less than half – Room for improvement.	Under 5 – Needs more work.
Cells				
Organ systems				
Nutrition and food tests				
The digestive system				
The heart				
Blood and circulation				
Movement				
The lungs and breathing				
Puberty and reproduction				
Drugs				
Fighting disease				
Photosynthesis				
Plant reproduction				
Carbon and nitrogen cycles				
Classification				
Variation				
Inheritance and genetics				
Food chains and webs				
Adaptation and competition				
Rocks				
The rock cycle				
Pollution				
States of matter				
Dissolving				
Particle theory				
Atoms and elements				
Metals				
Unusual elements				
Chemical reactions				
Reactivity series				
Displacement reactions				
Acids and alkalis				
Making salts				
Chemical tests				
Mixtures				
Separation techniques				
Compounds				
Naming compounds				
Balancing equations				
Speed				
Graphs of motion				
Forces				
Friction and terminal velocity				
Moments				
Pressure				
Light rays and reflection				
Refraction and colour				
Sounds				
Echoes and hearing				
Energy				
Using energy resources				
Alternative sources of energy				
Heat transfer				
Circuit components				
Circuits: current and voltage				
Magnets and electromagnets				
The Solar System 1				
The Solar System 2				

Cells

Cells are the building blocks of life. All living things are made up of cells. A living thing is called an organism. Plants and animals are organisms.

A Choose just one answer, a, b, c or d.

1 What do animal and plant cells have in common?
a) cell membrane, nucleus   **(1 mark)**
b) cell membrane, cell wall
c) vacuole, nucleus
d) cell wall, nucleus

2 What is a cell membrane for?   **(1 mark)**
a) controlling the activities of the cell
b) it is where chemical reactions take place
c) controlling what passes in and out of the cell
d) to contain genes

3 A group of cells carrying out the same job is called: **(1 mark)**
a) specialised cell   b) tissue
c) organ   d) organ system

4 Why do palisade cells contain so many chloroplasts?   **(1 mark)**
a) for extra support
b) to absorb sunlight for photosynthesis
c) to help them absorb water
d) to keep the leaf in shape

5 What shape best describes a red blood cell?
        (1 mark)
a) spherical
b) square
c) oval
d) biconcave

Score   /5

B Answer all parts of all questions.

1 Fill in the missing labels of this plant cell.   **(3 marks)**

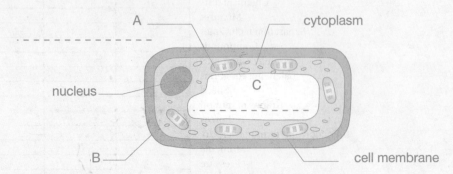

A
cytoplasm
nucleus
C
B
cell membrane

2 Put a tick in the box if you think the cell contains the part.   **(12 marks)**

	chloroplasts	nucleus	cell wall	mitochondria
Onion cell		✓	✓	✓
Palisade cell	✓	✓	✓	✓
Human skin cell		✓		✓

Score   /15

C These are SATs-style questions. Answer all parts of the questions.

The diagram below shows a red blood cell.

biconcave discs

cross section

1 a) A red blood cell is an animal cell, but what feature does it not have that all other animal cells have? *(2 marks)*

...................A nucleus...

....

b) What is the function of this type of cell? *(1 mark)*

......................carry oxygen..

....

c) A plant cell has a cell wall as well as a cell membrane. What is the function of a cell wall? *(1 mark)*

....

d) A plant cell also contains chloroplasts. What is the function of chloroplasts? *(1 mark)*

....

....

e) Name two specialised plant cells. *(1 mark)*

..........Root hair cell · Palisade cell................................

2 Red blood cells are specialised animal cells. Name 3 other specialised animal cells. *(3 marks)*

...........Sperm cell...

...........Phph cell..

...........Nerve cell..

Score /9

Organ systems

Plants can be divided up into five main parts. The five parts work together so that the plant can carry out the seven life processes. Humans have nine organ systems that enable them to carry out the life processes.

A Choose just one answer, a, b, c or d.

1 What are the tubes called that carry water to the leaf? (1 mark)
- a) phloem
- b) xylem
- c) stem
- d) root

2 Where does photosynthesis take place? (1 mark)
- a) the flower
- b) the root
- c) the stem
- d) the leaf

3 What are stomata? (1 mark)
- a) holes on the top of the leaf
- b) a type of tomato
- c) a type of seed
- d) holes on the underside of the leaf

4 What does the endocrine system do? (1 mark)
- a) sends messages around the body
- b) gets rid of waste
- c) produces hormones
- d) digests food

5 Which organ turns waste products into urine? (1 mark)
- a) bladder
- b) lungs
- c) kidney
- d) heart

Score   /5

B Answer all parts of all questions.

1 Label this diagram of a flowering plant __and__ state the function of each part. (8 marks)

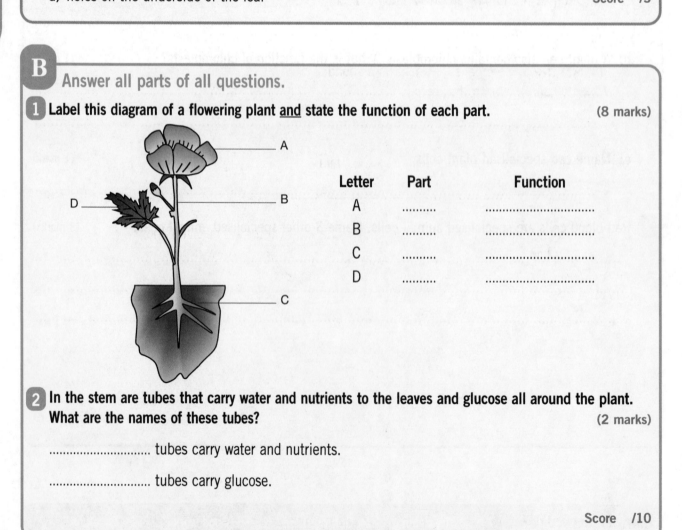

Letter	Part	Function
A	....	....
B	....	....
C	....	....
D	....	....

2 In the stem are tubes that carry water and nutrients to the leaves and glucose all around the plant. What are the names of these tubes? (2 marks)

.... tubes carry water and nutrients.

.... tubes carry glucose.

Score   /10

8

C These are SATs-style questions. Answer all parts of all questions.

The diagram shows an organ system in the human body

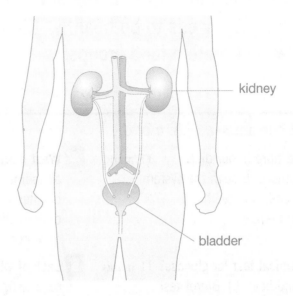

kidney

bladder

1 a) Which organ system is shown in the diagram above? (1 mark)

....

b) Which organ in the diagram above stores urine? (1 mark)

....

2 a) We have five sense organs that help us respond to changes in the environment. Which organ system do they belong to? (1 mark)

....

b) How are the sense organs connected to the brain? (1 mark)

....

c) Describe another organ system in the body; state what organs are involved and their function. (3 marks)

....

....

....

....

Score   /7

How well did you do?   1–4 **Try again**   5–8 **Getting there**   9–15 **Good work**   16–22 **Excellent!**

Nutrition and food tests

A balanced diet consists of seven food groups. These provide all the nutrients that the body needs to be healthy. There are chemical tests for the carbohydrate, fat and protein food groups.

A Choose just one answer, a, b, c or d.

1 Why do we need fibre in our diet? **(1 mark)**
   a) to help food move through the system
   b) for healthy bones and teeth
   c) for growth and repair
   d) for energy

2 What is the chemical test for glucose? **(1 mark)**
   a) Benedict's and heat b) Biuret test
   c) iodine solution   d) Benedict's Solution

3 Why do we need protein in our diet? **(1 mark)**
   a) for healthy bones and teeth
   b) for energy
   c) for energy storage
   d) for growth and repair

4 What is the chemical test for protein? **(1 mark)**
   a) iodine solution
   b) Biuret test
   c) Benedict's Solution
   d) water

5 Lack of vitamins and minerals causes: **(1 mark)**
   a) constipation
   b) diarrhoea
   c) deficiency diseases
   d) lack of energy

Score   /5

B Answer all parts of the question.

1 The following passage is about the seven major food groups and the chemical tests for them.
Fill in the gaps. **(16 marks)**

The seven food groups are ...., ..., ..., ..., ..., fibre and water.

The food group that provides us with energy and contains foods such as pasta and bread is the .... group. This group contains two food types: sugars and ....

Proteins are needed for growth and .... of cells. Fats are needed as an energy .... and for insulation.

The chemical test for starch is .... solution. If there is starch present then it changes from a yellow/brown colour to a ..../............. colour.

The chemical test for glucose is Benedict's solution and .... If sugar is present the solution turns from blue to ....

The chemical test for protein is the .... test. A positive result for protein is a colour change to ....

We need fibre in our diet to help move food through the gut and prevent .... Vitamins and minerals are needed in small amounts and are essential for good health.

Score   /16

C This is a SATs-style question. Answer all parts of the question.

1 The table below shows the recommended daily amounts of nutrients and energy for different groups of people.

	Energy in kJ	Protein in g	Carbohydrate in g	Fat in g
Male 12–15	11 700	55	350	110
Female 12–15	9 700	45	275	80
Manual worker 20–50	15 000	55	350	100
Office worker 20–50	11 000	55	300	95
Pregnant female	10 000	80	280	80

a) Which two types of nutrient provide us with the most energy in our diet? (2 marks)

....

....

b) Explain why the manual worker needs to eat more carbohydrate than the office worker. (1 mark)

....

c) Why do we need protein in our diets? (1 mark)

....

d) Explain why the pregnant female needs more protein than the other groups of people. (1 mark)

....

....

e) Account for the difference in energy needs between girls and boys of the same age. (1 mark)

....

f) Why might the amount of energy needed by two girls of the same age be different? (2 marks)

....

Score /8

The digestive system

- The digestive system is really one long tube called the gut. If it were unravelled it would be about nine metres long!
- Digestion begins with the mouth and ends at the anus.
- It normally takes food 24–28 hours to pass through your digestive system.

A — Choose just one answer, a, b, c or d.

1 Which enzyme digests fats? (1 mark)
a) protease   b) lipase
c) carbohydrase   d) amylase

2 What is bile? (1 mark)
a) a type of cell
b) a type of tooth
c) a solution that helps break down fats
d) a food droplet

3 What do proteins get broken down into?
a) amino acids   b) glucose (1 mark)
c) starch   d) fatty acids

4 What are conditions like in the stomach?
a) alkaline (1 mark)
b) neutral
c) cold
d) acidic

5 What do large insoluble molecules get broken down into? (1 mark)
a) large soluble molecules
b) small soluble molecules
c) medium soluble molecules
d) small insoluble molecules

Score /5

B — Answer all parts of all questions.

1 The three main types of enzyme are carbohydrases, lipases and proteases. They digest large food molecules into glucose, fatty acids and glycerol, and amino acids.

a) Which type of enzymes digest protein and what does it digest protein into? (2 marks)

....

b) Which type of enzymes digest carbohydrates and what does it digest carbohydrates into? (2 marks)

....

c) Which type of enzymes digest fats and what does it digest fats into? (2 marks)

....

2 Cross out the incorrect words in this definition of digestion. (4 marks)

Digestion is the breaking down of large/small, soluble/insoluble food molecules into small/large, soluble/insoluble food molecules so that they can pass into the blood stream.

3 List the organs that food passes through until digestion is completed. (4 marks)

....
....

Score /14

C These are SATs-style questions. Answer all parts of all questions.

A scientist was investigating the best conditions for the digestion of protein. He used three flasks, each containing some egg white which made the liquid cloudy. The diagrams below show the conditions in each flask.

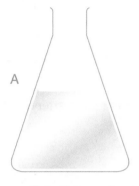

Egg white and pepsin

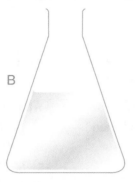

Egg white, pepsin and hydrochloric acid

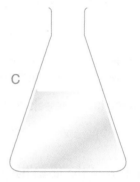

Egg white, boiled pepsin and hydrochloric acid

1 **a)** After 6 hours flask B was clear and not cloudy. What does this suggest had happened? (1 mark)

....

b) What type of substance is pepsin? (1 mark)

....

c) What effect does boiling have on the activity of pepsin? (1 mark)

....

d) All the flasks were kept at 37°C. Explain why. (1 mark)

....

e) What does this experiment prove about the conditions needed for the digestion of protein? (2 marks)

....

....

2 **a)** Where in the body would you find conditions like that of flask B? (1 mark)

....

b) During digestion, what does protein get broken down into? (1 mark)

....

Score /8

How well did you do?   1–7 **Try again**   8–12 **Getting there**   13–19 **Good work**   20–27 **Excellent!**

The heart

The heart and blood vessels are the transport system of the body. They provide the body with oxygen and nutrients and take away waste products. The types of blood vessel look different because they have different functions.

A Choose just one answer, a, b, c or d.

1 How many blood vessels leave the heart?
   a) 3   b) 2   **(1 mark)**
   c) 1   d) 4

2 Which part of the heart has the thickest walls?   **(1 mark)**
   a) left atrium   b) right ventricle
   c) right atrium   d) left ventricle

3 Which side of the heart receives oxygenated blood?   **(1 mark)**
   a) right   b) left
   c) all parts   d) no parts

4 What is the name of the main artery?   **(1 mark)**
   a) pulmonary artery
   b) pulmonary vein
   c) aorta
   d) vena cava

5 Which blood vessels deliver oxygen and nutrients to the heart itself?   **(1 mark)**
   a) pulmonary arteries
   b) pulmonary veins
   c) coronary arteries
   d) vena cava

Score /5

B Answer all parts of all questions.

1 Match up the blood vessel with its description.   **(3 marks)**

Vein   Carries deoxygenated and oxygenated blood, has very thin walls.

Artery   Carries blood towards the heart at low pressure, contains valves.

Capillary   Carries blood away from the heart at high pressure, has thick walls.

2 Decide whether the statements about the heart and its blood vessels are true or false.   **(6 marks)**

The right side of the heart receives oxygenated blood.   ....

The left side of the heart has thicker walls than the right.   ....

The valves in the heart prevent the blood flowing backwards.   ....

The pulmonary vein collects oxygen from the lungs.   ....

The vena cava is the main artery of the body.   ....

The blood leaves the left side of the heart to go to the body.   ....

Score /9

C These are SATs-style questions. Answer all parts of all questions.

The diagram shows the blood vessels entering and leaving the heart.

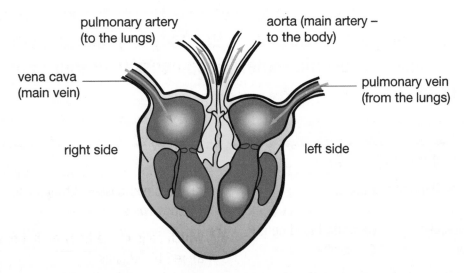

1 **a) What is the job of the heart?** (1 mark)

....

....

b) Which type of blood vessels takes blood away from the heart? (1 mark)

....

....

c) Which blood vessel leaves the heart to collect oxygen from the lungs? (1 mark)

....

....

d) Which side of the heart contains blood rich in oxygen? (1 mark)

....

....

2 **a) Give one difference in structure between an artery and a vein.** (1 mark)

....

....

b) What is the name of the smallest blood vessels not shown on the diagram? (1 mark)

....

....

Score   /6

How well did you do?   ✗ 1–4 **Try again**   5–9 **Getting there**   10–14 **Good work**   15–20 **Excellent!** ✓

Blood and circulation

Blood flows around the body in blood vessels. The heart provides the force needed for this. The path taken around the body is called the circulatory system and it follows a specific route. Blood consists of four parts, each with its own job in the body.

A Choose just one answer, a, b, c or d.

1 Which part of the blood is mainly water? (1 mark)
a) red blood cells   b) white blood cells
c) platelets   d) plasma

2 Where does the aorta take the blood? (1 mark)
a) to the lungs   b) towards the body
c) to the heart   d) to the veins

3 Why is the human circulation called a double circulation? (1 mark)
a) the blood passes through the heart twice
b) the blood travels twice as fast as in other circulations
c) the blood takes twice as long as other circulations
d) the blood passes through each part of the body twice

4 Which cells of the body do not have a nucleus?
a) red blood cells (1 mark)
b) white blood cells
c) sperm cells
d) all cells have a nucleus

5 Which side of the heart carries oxygenated blood? (1 mark)
a) right
b) both sides
c) neither side
d) left

Score /5

B Answer all parts of all questions.

1 Which cells in the blood do not contain a nucleus? (1 mark)

....

2 The plasma is the liquid part of the blood. The diagram opposite shows the other three components of blood that float in the plasma.

Name each blood component and give its function.

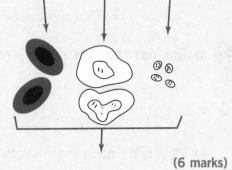

Letter	Name	Function
A	....	....
B	....	....
C	....	....

(6 marks)

3 The blood passes through our body in a system called the circulatory system. We have a double circulatory system. Why is it called this and what are the two pathways that blood takes? (3 marks)

....

....

Score /10

C These are SATs-style questions. Answer all parts of the questions.

1 a) Red blood cells carry oxygen around the body. Explain how a high number of red blood cells helps an athlete during a race. (2 marks)

....

....

b) Red blood cells contain a substance that helps them carry oxygen. What is the name of this substance? (1 mark)

....

2 a) The blood flows to the lungs to collect oxygen in the circulatory system. Which of the following shows the correct route taken by the blood on its way to the lungs and back to the heart? Tick the correct line. (1 mark)

pulmonary artery – lungs – pulmonary vein – heart   ....

lungs – pulmonary artery – pulmonary vein – heart   ....

pulmonary vein – lungs – pulmonary artery – heart   ....

b) Name the waste substance that is transported back to the lungs from the cells in the body. (1 mark)

....

c) Glucose is a useful substance needed by the body. Which part of the blood carries glucose? Tick the correct answer. (1 mark)

Plasma   ....

Red blood cells   ....

White blood cells   ....

Platelets   ....

d) Name one other substance carried by the plasma around the body. (1 mark)

....

Score   /7

How well did you do?   1–4 Try again   5–8 Getting there   9–15 Good work   16–22 Excellent!

Movement

The human body is able to move because of the skeleton, muscles and joints. The central nervous system controls this movement with the use of sense organs.

A Choose just one answer, a, b, c or d.

1 Your hip joint is: (1 mark)
a) a ball and socket joint
b) a fixed joint
c) a hinge joint
d) a partly moveable joint

2 A reflex action is: (1 mark)
a) a slow response
b) a quick response
c) an action that needs thought
d) an action that does not involve sense organs

3 Which is the largest bone in the body? (1 mark)
a) rib   b) humerus
c) femur   d) radius

4 The hips are also known as the: (1 mark)
a) patella   b) humerus
c) pelvis   d) fibula

5 Which of these joints is an example of a synovial joint? (1 mark)
a) skull joint
b) spine
c) all joints are synovial joints
d) hip joint

Score   /5

B Answer all parts of all questions.

1 Fill in the missing words using those listed below. (8 marks)

ligaments   muscles   joint   tendons   biceps   triceps   central nervous system   cartilage

The skeleton is made up of bones that protect many organs in your body. When two bones meet, a

.... is formed. .... provide the force to move bones at joints. At the ends of bones is a layer

of smooth .... This acts as a shock absorber. The bones are attached to muscles by ....

and the bones are held together by strong fibres called .... Muscles work in pairs to produce

movement. An example of a muscle pair is the .... and .... The overall control of

movement is from the .... This uses the five sense organs to respond to

changes in the environment.

2 What are the three functions of the skeleton? (3 marks)

....

3 When we touch something hot we tend to move our hand away very quickly. What is this type of reaction called? (1 mark)

....

Score   /12

C These are SATs-style questions. Answer all parts of all questions.

The diagram shows the knee joint.

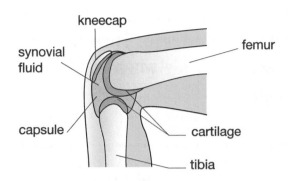

1 a) Osteoarthritis is a painful condition that causes small pieces of cartilage to wear away and break off. Suggest two effects this could have on the joint. (2 marks)

....

....

b) What feature not shown on the diagram holds bones together? (1 mark)

....

....

c) What provides the necessary force to move bones at the joints? (1 mark)

....

....

2 a) Muscles work in pairs to produce movement. What are the names of the muscles that work together to bend and straighten the arm? (2 marks)

....

....

b) Which muscle relaxes when the arm is straightened? (1 mark)

....

c) Which muscle contracts when the arm is straightened? (1 mark)

....

Score   /8

How well did you do?   1–6 **Try again**   7–12 **Getting there**   13–18 **Good work**   19–25 **Excellent!**

The lungs and breathing

- The lungs are two big air sacs in your upper body.
- Their job is to supply oxygen to your cells when you breathe in and get rid of the waste product carbon dioxide when you breathe out.
- This is called gas exchange.

A   Choose just one answer, a, b, c or d.

1 What is respiration?   (1 mark)
a) breathing in
b) a chemical reaction that uses glucose and oxygen
c) breathing out
d) a plant's way of making food

2 What are the products of respiration?   (1 mark)
a) glucose and energy
b) oxygen, glucose and energy
c) carbon dioxide, water and energy
d) carbon dioxide and energy

3 Which of these factors is important for gas exchange?   (1 mark)
a) thick walled alveoli   b) thin walled alveoli
c) large alveoli   d) small alveoli

4 The trachea branches into two: (1 mark)
a) bronchi   b) bronchioles
c) alveoli   d) ribs

5 Emphysema causes the alveoli to: (1 mark)
a) get larger
b) stay the same size
c) get smaller
d) reduce in surface area

Score   /5

B   Answer all parts of all questions.

1 The diagram opposite shows part of the breathing system

Air sac surrounded by blood capilleries

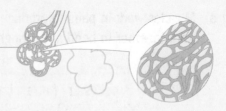

a) What is the name for air sacs like the one shown in the diagram?.................... (1 mark)

b) What is the name of the small tube leading into the air sac? .... (1 mark)

c) What takes place at the air sacs? .... (1 mark)

d) What gases are exchanged between the blood capillaries and the air sacs? .... (1 mark)

....

e) The air sacs and the blood capillary membranes are very thin. Give one other feature of the air sacs that helps the efficient exchange of gases.   (1 mark)

....

2 The following is an account of breathing in. Cross out the incorrect words.   (4 marks)

When you breathe in the intercostal muscles and the diaphragm muscle contract/relax. The ribs move up/down and out/in. The volume in the thorax increases/decreases and air rushes into the lungs.

Score   /9

C These are SATs-style questions. Answer all parts of all questions.

The diagram below shows part of the respiratory system.

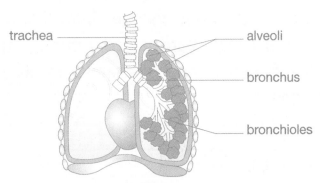

trachea — — alveoli

— bronchus

— bronchioles

1 **a)** List in order the parts of the respiratory system that air passes through until gaseous exchange occurs. (1 mark)

....

....

b) The purpose of the respiratory system is gas exchange with the blood. Where does gas exchange actually take place? (1 mark)

....

....

c) Which gas passes into the blood from the lungs? (1 mark)

....

....

d) Which gas passes into the lungs from the blood? (1 mark)

....

....

2 **a)** Breathing is necessary for respiration as it provides oxygen. What other substance is needed for respiration to take place? (1 mark)

....

....

b) Where does respiration actually take place? (1 mark)

....

....

c) Respiration releases energy. What is this energy used for? (1 mark)

....

Score   /7

How well did you do?   1–4 Try again   5–9 Getting there   10–16 Good work   17–21 Excellent!

Puberty and reproduction

Adolescence is a time when the body changes from that of a child to that of an adult. Emotional and physical changes occur during puberty. The male and female reproductive systems undergo changes in preparation for the possibility of reproduction.

A   Choose just one answer, a, b, c or d.

1 Which one of these is a male
hormone?   **(1 mark)**
a) oestrogen   b) progesterone
c) testosterone   d) urethra

2 On what day of the menstrual cycle does
an egg get released from the ovary?   **(1 mark)**
a) day 5   b) day 28
c) day 11   d) day 14

3 Why does the uterus lining thicken in
the menstrual cycle?   **(1 mark)**
a) to prepare for implantation
b) to protect the vagina
c) to prepare for menstruation
d) to stop an egg being released

4 How is the baby provided with oxygen
and nutrients?   **(1 mark)**
a) fallopian tube
b) umbilical cord
c) amniotic fluid
d) cervix

5 How are identical twins formed?   **(1 mark)**
a) two eggs are fertilised
b) fertilised egg divides in two
c) two sperms fertilise an egg
d) one sperm fertilises two eggs

Score   /5

B   Answer all parts of the question.

1 Label the male and female reproductive organs.

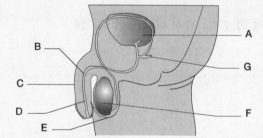
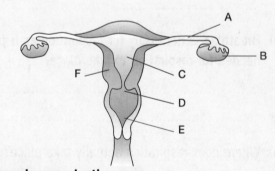

Male reproductive organs

A ....

B ....

C ....

D ....

E ....

F ....

G ....`

Female reproductive organs

A ....

B ....

C ....

D ....

E ....

F ....

Score   /13

C These are SATs-style questions. Answer all parts of all questions.

The diagram shows a baby developing in its mother's uterus.

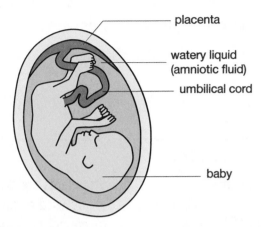

- placenta
- watery liquid (amniotic fluid)
- umbilical cord
- baby

1 a) The growing baby needs protecting from bumps, knocks, micro-organisms and harmful chemicals whilst in the mother's uterus. Describe how the baby is protected inside the mother's body.   (2 marks)

....

....

b) Through which labelled parts does the baby receive nutrients and oxygen from its mother whilst in the uterus?   (1 mark)

....

....

c) What happens to the walls of the uterus when the baby is ready to be born?   (1 mark)

....

....

2 In a girl's body, a chemical called a hormone is produced during adolescence, which causes changes.

a) Where is this hormone produced?   (1 mark)

....

....

b) Describe one change caused by this hormone.   (1 mark)

....

....

Score   /6

How well did you do?   ✗ 1–4 Try again   5–9 Getting there   10–16 Good work   17–24 Excellent! ✓

Drugs

- Smoking and solvents damage health without a doubt.
- Alcohol and drugs are also dangerous if misused.
- To keep healthy you need to eat a balanced diet, take regular exercise and avoid health risks.

A   Choose just one answer, a, b, c or d.

1 Which part of the body do drugs mostly affect? (1 mark)
- a) stomach
- b) blood vessels
- c) brain
- d) lungs

2 Sedatives are drugs that: (1 mark)
- a) slow reactions
- b) speed up reactions
- c) give you energy
- d) cause hallucinations

3 Hallucinogens are drugs that: (1 mark)
- a) are used as painkillers
- b) cause hallucinations
- c) are used to treat stress and anxiety
- d) slow down your reactions

4 Stimulants are drugs that: (1 mark)
- a) are used as painkillers
- b) are not harmful
- c) make you alert and awake
- d) slow down your reactions

5 The effects of solvents are similar to which other drugs? (1 mark)
- a) sedatives
- b) stimulants
- c) smoking
- d) alcohol

Score   /5

B   Answer all parts of the question.

1 Match up these facts with the following drugs. (7 marks)

sedative   hallucinogen   painkiller   stimulant   alcohol   solvent   cigarette

Facts

A depressant that slows the body's reactions. It causes a disease called cirrhosis. ....

It contains many harmful chemical substances and is very addictive. It contributes to a disease called emphysema. ....

This drug can give you extreme energy and also dehydration. It causes you to imagine things that are not really there. ....

It slows down the brain and alters reaction times. It can be used to treat stress and anxiety. ....

It speeds up the brain and nervous system. Addiction is high and withdrawal has many side effects including depression. ....

This drug is used to treat pain. Misuse can lead to infectious diseases and it can be addictive. ....

This drug affects the lungs, brain, kidneys and liver. It can cause loss of control and unconsciousness. ....

Score   /7

C These are SATs-style questions. Answer all parts of the questions.

1 The following apparatus was set up in class to separate the chemicals in cigarette smoke. As the cigarette burns the chemicals pass through the apparatus towards the lime water.

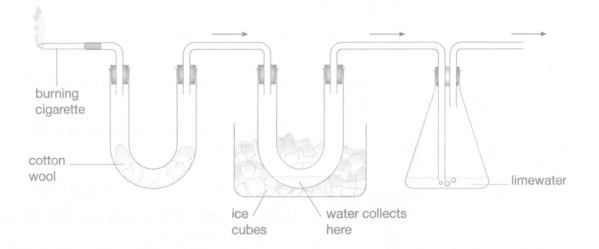

a) What brown sticky substance contained in cigarette smoke collects on the cotton wool? (1 mark)

....

b) What disease does this substance cause? (1 mark)

....

c) A chemical passes through the limewater. The lime water turns cloudy. What is this chemical? (1 mark)

....

d) Give the name of one other chemical in cigarette smoke and say how it is harmful. (2 marks)

....

....

2 a) What is the name of the disease caused by alcohol that affects the liver? (1 mark)

....

b) Is alcohol a depressant or a stimulant? (1 mark)

....

Score   /7

How well did you do?   ✗ 1–5 **Try again**   6–10 **Getting there**   11–15 **Good work**   16–19 **Excellent!** ✓

Fighting disease

- Microbes are bacteria, viruses and fungi.
- Not all microbes cause disease; some are useful.
- Microbes that get inside you and make you ill are called germs.

A Choose just one answer, a, b, c or d.

1 Which type of microbe produces toxins?
a) fungi   b) virus   **(1 mark)**
c) all of them   d) bacteria

2 Which of the following is caused by a virus?
a) whooping cough   b) HIV   **(1 mark)**
c) athlete's foot   d) tetanus

3 Which of the following cells do not have a nucleus?   **(1 mark)**
a) white blood cells   b) viruses
c) sperm cells   d) palisade cells

4 Which type of microbe is used for making beer and wine?   **(1 mark)**
a) bacteria   b) virus
c) fungi   d) virus and fungi

5 Which type of cell produces antitoxins? **(1 mark)**
a) red blood cells
b) bacteria
c) white blood cells
d) virus

Score   /5

B Answer all parts of all questions.

1 a) Give three ways in which disease-causing bacteria can enter your body.   **(3 marks)**

....

....

....

b) How do white blood cells fight off the bacteria that enter your body?   **(2 marks)**

....

2 Sometimes white blood cells need extra help in fighting disease. What extra help are we able to get a) before and b) after the bacteria enter our body?

a) .... **(1 mark)**

b) .... **(1 mark)**

3 Name the two other types of microbe that may cause disease.   **(2 marks)**

....

4 Unscramble these words to give the names of some infectious diseases.   **(4 marks)**

nteaust   t...................   sotbeculsuir   t...................

nhcekic xpo   c.......... p........   leaesms   m...................

Score   /13

C These are SATs-style questions. Answer all parts of all questions.

1 Viruses are very small microbes and have a very simple structure.

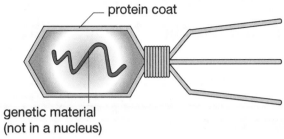

protein coat

genetic material
(not in a nucleus)

a) Give one similarity between the structure of a bacterial cell and a virus.   (1 mark)

....

....

b) Give one difference between the structure of a bacterial cell and a virus.   (1 mark)

....

....

c) The body can use its natural defence mechanisms to fight viruses. Describe how
vaccines help the body's fight against viruses.   (2 marks)

....

....

2 a) A scientist was investigating the conditions that bacteria that live in the human body need to
reproduce by growing bacteria in petri dishes on the surface of jelly. The petri dishes were
kept at different temperatures. Tick the correct box to show the temperature at which the
bacteria would reproduce rapidly.   (1 mark)

100°C ☐

−20°C ☐

10°C   ☐

37°C   ☐

b) Give two safety precautions that the scientist should take when using bacteria in his
experiments.   (2 marks)

1 ....

....

2 ....

....

Score   /7

How well did you do?   ✗ 1–6 **Try again**   7–12 **Getting there**   13–18 **Good work**   19–25 **Excellent!** ✓

Photosynthesis

Photosynthesis is a chemical process that plants use to make their food (glucose) using energy from the Sun. It occurs in the leaves.

A Choose just one answer, a, b, c or d.

1 When does photosynthesis take place? (1 mark)
- a) during the day
- b) at night
- c) night and day
- d) in the winter

2 Which part of the plant carres water up to the leaf? (1 mark)
- a) phloem
- b) stomata
- c) xylem
- d) palisade cells

3 Which type of cell contains many chloroplasts? (1 mark)
- a) phloem
- b) stomata
- c) xylem
- d) palisade cells

4 What mineral is needed for a plant to make protein? (1 mark)
- a) potassium
- b) phosphate
- c) calcium
- d) nitrate

5 What are the symptoms if a plant lacks potassium? (1 mark)
- a) yellow leaves and dead spots
- b) poor root growth
- c) purple young leaves
- d) stunted growth

Score /5

B Answer all parts of all questions.

1 Draw lines connecting the minerals with their deficiency symptoms. (3 marks)

Nitrate   Poor root growth and purple young leaves

Phosphate   Yellow leaves with dead spots

Potassium   Stunted growth and yellow older leaves

2 The diagram shows a labelled section of a leaf. Answer the questions that follow using words from the diagram. (4 marks)

waterproof layer

palisade cells

leaf vein

stoma

a) This part of the leaf contains the most chloroplasts needed for photosynthesis. ....

b) This part of the leaf allows carbon dioxide into the leaf. ....

c) This part of the leaf prevents too much water leaving the leaf. ....

d) This part of the leaf contains the xylem and phloem tubes. ....

Score /7

C

These are SATs-style questions. Answer all parts of all questions.

1 The diagram below shows an experiment to study photosynthesis in pondweed.

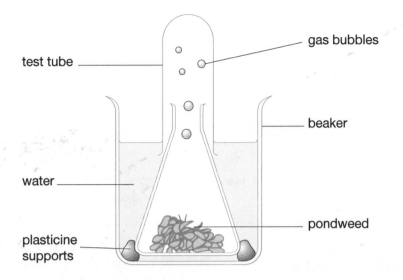

a) During the experiment bubbles of gas are seen collecting in the test tube. Which gas is produced? (1 mark)

....

b) How can you prove what the gas bubbles are? (1 mark)

....

c) The pondweed needs certain conditions to produce the bubbles of gas. What are these conditions? (2 marks)

....

....

d) What substance other than the gas is produced during photosynthesis? (1 mark)

....

2 The leaves of the pondweed were removed, boiled in water, then in ethanol, and then washed. Iodine solution was added to the leaf.

a) The leaf changed colour when iodine was added. What colour did it become? (1 mark)

....

b) What did this colour change show had been produced in the leaf? (1 mark)

....

Score   /7

How well did you do?   1–5 Try again   6–10 Getting there   11–15 Good work   16–19 Excellent!

For more help on this topic see KS3 Science Success Guide pages 26–27 & 72

29

Plant reproduction

- Plants have male and female sex cells just like animals.
- They reproduce by forming seeds inside fruits.
- Reproduction consists of pollination, fertilisation, seed dispersal, and germination.

A Choose just one answer, a, b, c or d.

1 Which one is the odd one out?   (1 mark)
   a) stigma   b) anther
   c) style   d) ovary

2 What do insect-pollinated plants have that wind-pollinated plants tend not to have?   (1 mark)
   a) long filaments   b) long stigmas
   c) bright petals   d) anthers

3 What is pollination?   (1 mark)
   a) a pollen nucleus fusing with an ovule
   b) pollen attaching to the stigma
   c) a pollen tube beginning to grow
   d) ovary turning into a fruit

4 When is fertilisation complete?   (1 mark)
   a) when a pollen grain attaches to a stigma
   b) when a pollen tube begins to grow
   c) when an ovary turns into a fruit
   d) when a pollen grain nucleus fuses with an ovule nucleus

5 Which is the odd one out?   (1 mark)
   a) stigma
   b) anther
   c) pollen
   d) filament

Score   /5

B Answer all parts of all questions.

1 The following are the reproductive parts of a flowering plant. First say whether they are male or female and state, for the last three, their function.   (8 marks)

Filament   ....

Style   ....

Stigma   ....

Ovary   ....

Anther   ....

2 Once seeds have been formed they need to be scattered (dispersed) so they have a good chance to grow into new plants. The diagrams show 3 types of plant. Say how each scatters its seeds. (3 marks)

Tomato   ....

Dandelion   ....

Sweet pea   ....

Score   /11

C This is a SATs-style question. Answer all parts of the question.

1 The pictures below show a wind-pollinated flower and an insect-pollinated flower.

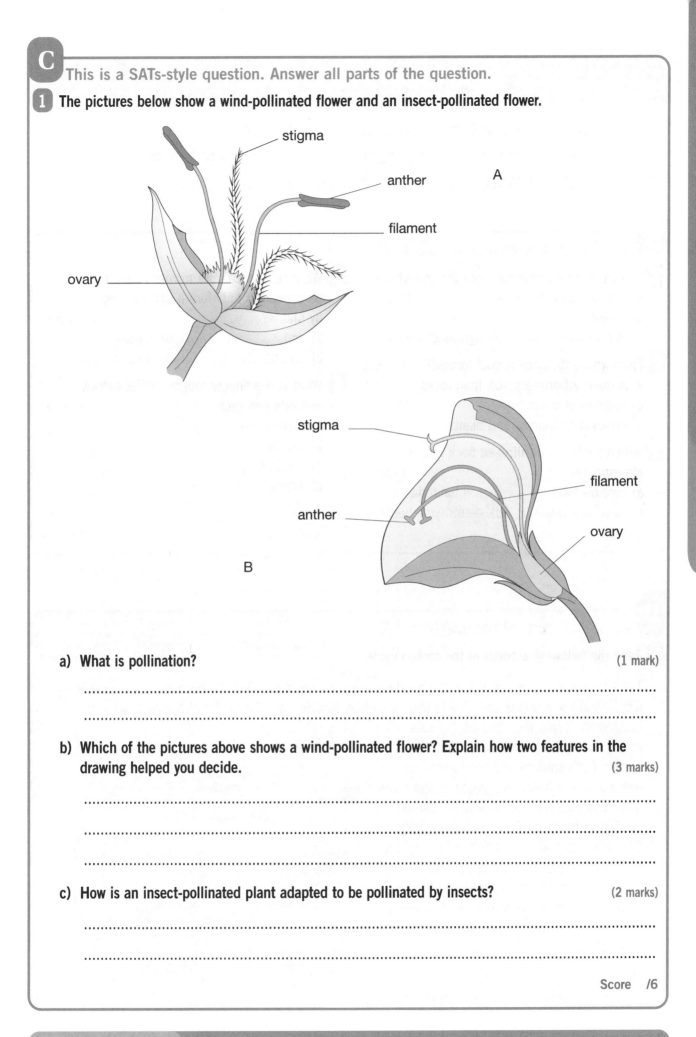

stigma

anther A

filament

ovary

stigma

filament

anther

ovary

B

a) What is pollination? (1 mark)

....

....

b) Which of the pictures above shows a wind-pollinated flower? Explain how two features in the drawing helped you decide. (3 marks)

....

....

....

c) How is an insect-pollinated plant adapted to be pollinated by insects? (2 marks)

....

....

Score   /6

How well did you do?   1–4 **Try again**   5–8 **Getting there**   9–15 **Good work**   16–22 **Excellent!** ✓

Carbon and nitrogen cycles

- Carbon dioxide and nitrogen are atmospheric gases.
- The amount of each gas in the atmosphere should stay the same, as they are constantly recycled in the environment.

A   Choose just one answer, a, b, c or d.

1 Carbon dioxide is released into the soil when:
a) animals and plants die   (1 mark)
b) it rains
c) earthquakes occur   d) lightning strikes

2 From what substance is coal formed?   (1 mark)
a) remains of animals   b) from rocks
c) remains of plants
d) remains of animals and plants

3 Which bacteria put nitrogen back into the atmosphere?   (1 mark)
a) root bacteria   b) soil bacteria
c) fungi bacteria   d) denitrifying bacteria

4 What substance does nitrogen have to be converted to before it can be used by plants?   (1 mark)
a) soil   b) nitrate
c) carbon   d) nitrogen gas

5 What is the energy source for the carbon and nitrogen cycle?   (1 mark)
a) fossil fuels
b) plants
c) the Sun
d) animals

Score   /5

B   Answer all parts of the question.

1 Read the following account of the carbon cycle.   (7 marks)

The amount of carbon dioxide in the air stays relatively constant (0.03%) because the carbon is recycled in the environment. Plants take in carbon dioxide from the air for photosynthesis and incorporate it into their bodies. Animals eating the plants get the carbon into their bodies. Both animals and plants produce waste and eventually die. Decomposers break down this material and release the carbon back into the atmosphere during respiration. Of course, animals and plants also carry out respiration whilst they are alive. Animals and plants that do not decay eventually become fossils. The fossils are burned as fuel and the carbon is released back into the atmosphere.

Use the underlined words to complete the numbered points in the diagram opposite.

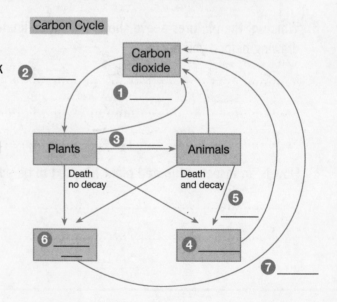

Carbon Cycle

Score   /7

32

C

This is a SATs-style question. Answer all parts of the question.

1 **The diagram below shows a simplified nitrogen cycle.**

Nitrogen Cycle

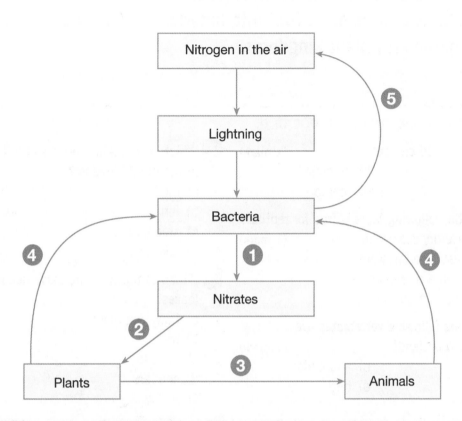

a) **Give a brief explanation of what is happening at each of the numbered stages.** (5 marks)

1. ....

2. ....

3. ....

4. ....

5. ....

b) **What do animals and plants need nitrogen for?** (1 mark)

....

c) **What conditions are needed for step 5 of the nitrogen cycle to take place?** (1 mark)

....

Score   /7

Classification

- Classification is used to sort out all living organisms into groups, according to the similarities between them.
- All living things are divided first into kingdoms – the two main ones are the animal and plant kingdoms.

A Choose just one answer, a, b, c or d.

1 Which is the odd one out?   (1 mark)
- a) bird
- b) mammal
- c) insect
- d) reptile

2 Which of the following facts is true for reptiles?
- a) they have dry scaly skin   (1 mark)
- b) they must breed in water
- c) they breathe through gills
- d) they have hair on their body

3 Which of the following vertebrates live in water and on land?   (1 mark)
- a) fish
- b) amphibian
- c) reptile
- d) bird

4 Which of the following does not belong in the plant kingdom?   (1 mark)
- a) moss
- b) fern
- c) arachnid
- d) conifer

5 Which of the following have needle-like leaves?   (1 mark)
- a) flowering plants
- b) ferns
- c) mosses
- d) conifers

Score /5

B Answer all parts of all questions.

1 Use the key to identify the following plants   (4 marks)

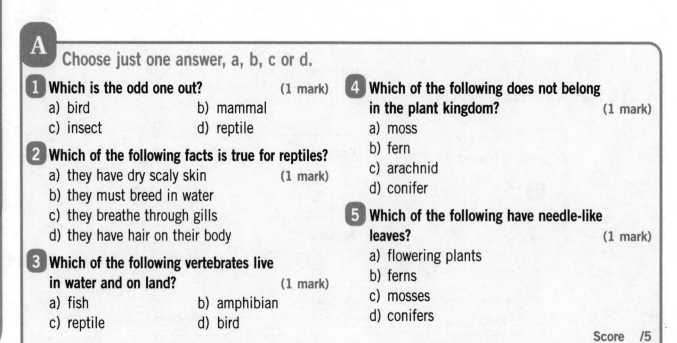

A   B   C   D

Start

leaf divided into five lobes | leaf not divided into five lobes

sycamore

edge of leaf smooth   edge of leaf not smooth

privet

edge of leaf toothed   edge of leaf rounded

silver birch   oak

A = ...   B = ...
C = ...   D = ...

2 Which is the odd one out?   (3 marks)

a) snail, spider, ladybird ....   b) leech, millipede, earthworm ....

c) daisy, moss, conifer ....

Score /7

34

C These are SATs-style questions. Answer all parts of all questions.

1 Classification is what scientists use to sort living things into groups. All living things are first divided into kingdoms. The animal kingdom may then be divided up into those with backbones and those without backbones.

a) What do we call animals with backbones? (1 mark)

....

b) What do we call animals without backbones? (1 mark)

....

The animals with backbones can be divided into the 5 groups below.

fish

amphibians

birds

reptiles

mammals

2 a) Give another example for each group and name a characteristic of each group. (10 marks)

(i) fish ....

(ii) mammals ....

(iii) birds ....

(iv) reptiles ....

(v) amphibians ....

Score /12

Variation

- All living things vary in the way they look or behave.
- Living things that belong to the same species are all slightly different.
- Living things that belong to different species are totally different.
- Inheritance, the environment or a combination of both may cause these differences.

A Choose just one answer, a, b, c or d.

1 How many chromosomes does a human sperm or egg cell have? **(1 mark)**
a) 46   b) 47
c) 20   d) 23

2 Where are chromosomes found?   **(1 mark)**
a) cell membrane   b) genes
c) vacuole   d) nucleus

3 Which of these is an inherited feature? **(1 mark)**
a) scars   b) blood group
c) speaking French d) having neat writing

4 How many chromosomes does a fertilised egg contain?   **(1 mark)**
a) 46   b) 23
c) 40   d) 20

5 What are our genes made of?   **(1 mark)**
a) chromosomes
b) cotton
c) DNA
d) polyester

Score   /5

B Answer all parts of all questions.

1 Which of these graphs shows a) discontinuous variation and b) continuous variation?   **(2 marks)**

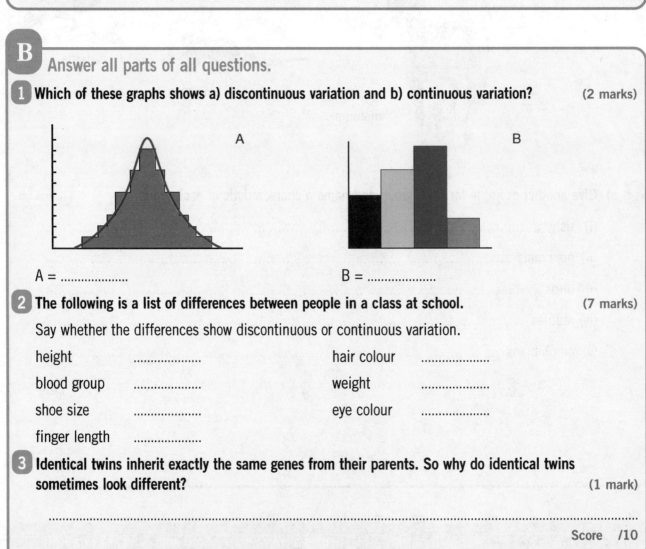

A = ...

B = ...

2 The following is a list of differences between people in a class at school.   **(7 marks)**

Say whether the differences show discontinuous or continuous variation.

height   ....   hair colour   ....

blood group   ....   weight   ....

shoe size   ....   eye colour   ....

finger length   ....

3 Identical twins inherit exactly the same genes from their parents. So why do identical twins sometimes look different?   **(1 mark)**

....

Score   /10

This is a SATs-style question. Answer all parts of the question.

1 The drawings below show a modern pig and a wild pig. The modern pig has descended from the wild pig.

modern pig

wild pig

a) The two types of pig are different in appearance to each other. What causes this variation? (1 mark)

....

....

b) A long time ago the modern pig was developed by farmers, by mating wild pigs together until the desired characteristics were produced. What term is used to describe this deliberate mating of animals? (1 mark)

....

....

c) Which features do you think the farmer wanted to breed out of the wild pig? (2 marks)

....

....

d) Which features do you think the farmers wanted to breed into the modern pig? (2 marks)

....

....

Score /6

How well did you do?   1–4 **Try again**   5–9 **Getting there**   10–16 **Good work**   17–21 **Excellent!**

Inheritance and genetics

- Genetics is the study of how information is passed on from generation to generation.
- Our genes, inherited from our parents, determine what we basically look like.

A   Choose just one answer, a, b, c or d.

1 Where are genes found? (1 mark)
a) on a chromosome
b) in the cell membrane
c) in the cytoplasm of animal cells
d) in the vacuole of plant cells

2 How many genes are there for each feature?
a) 4   b) 3   (1 mark)
c) 6   d) 2

3 Which of the following could be a cause of mutation? (1 mark)
a) sleeping   b) exercise
c) radiation   d) eating

4 What is sickle cell anaemia? (1 mark)
a) a disease of the white blood cells
b) a disease of the platelets
c) a disease of the red blood cells
d) a disease affecting farmers

5 How many genes for each feature do we inherit from each parent? (1 mark)
a) 2
b) 1
c) 4
d) 3

Score /5

B   Answer all parts of all questions.

1 Fill in the gaps using the words provided. (8 marks)

dominant   recessive   chromosomes   genes   pairs   DNA   mutation   radiation

Inside a cell is the nucleus, which controls all our inherited features. Inside the nucleus are thread-like …………. On the chromosomes are …………. of …………. Humans have 46 chromosomes. The genes are made up of a chemical called …………. We inherit two genes for every feature. Genes can be more powerful and called …………. or less powerful and called …………. Occasionally during the inheritance process things can go wrong. This is called a …………. The chances of this happening are increased by exposure to certain chemicals and ………….

2 A red-flowered rose was crossed with a white-flowered rose. The seeds were grown and all grew into red roses.

a) Which colour gene was dominant? ……………………………………………… (1 mark)

b) What could be the gene combination (genotype) of the offspring Rr or rr? ……………………………………………… (1 mark)

c) When the offspring were fertilised together there were three times as many red roses as white roses. Show this in a punnet square diagram. (3 marks)

sperm / eggs

Score /13

38

C

These are SATs-style questions. Answer all parts of all questions.

1 Our genes that we inherit from our parents determine what we will look like.

a) What other important factor contributes to what we look like? (1 mark)

....

b) Which part of an animal cell contains the genes? (1 mark)

....

c) Genes are found on chromosomes. How many chromosomes does a typical human body cell have? (1 mark)

....

d) A body cell of a mouse contains 40 chromosomes. How many chromosomes will a sperm cell of a mouse contain? (1 mark)

....

2 There are two genes for features such as eye colour. We inherit one gene from each parent. We can show the inheritance of a particular feature using a punnet square.

Look at this punnet square and answer the questions that follow.

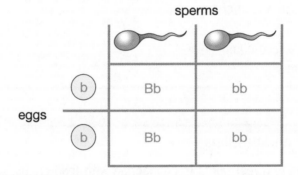

sperms

eggs

b	Bb	bb
b	Bb	bb

The genes for brown eyes are dominant **BB** or **Bb**.

The genes for blue eyes are recessive **bb**.

a) How many brown-eyed children would you expect? (1 mark)

....

b) How many blue-eyed children would you expect? (1 mark)

....

c) What was the father's genotype (combination of genes)? (1 mark)

....

Score   /7

Food chains and webs

- Food chains and webs begin with energy from the Sun.
- A food chain shows us what eats what in a community.
- A food web is made up of interconnected food chains.

A Choose just one answer, a, b, c or d.

1 What do the arrows in a food chain show?
  a) chemical reactions   (1 mark)
  b) passing of time
  c) transfer of food energy
  d) direction of movement

2 What does a pyramid of numbers
  show?   (1 mark)
  a) the numbers involved in a food chain
  b) the mass involved in a food chain
  c) a linked food chain
  d) simply who eats whom

3 What does a pyramid of biomass show? (1 mark)
  a) the numbers involved in a food chain
  b) a linked food chain
  c) the mass involved in a food chain
  d) simply who eats whom

4 In the food chain grass, rabbit, fox,
  which are consumers?   (1 mark)
  a) grass
  b) rabbit only
  c) fox only
  d) rabbit and fox

5 Why do the masses in a food chain get
  less at each level?   (1 mark)
  a) animals only eat one thing
  b) loss of energy
  c) plants cannot produce enough food
  d) the animals at the top cannot eat more

Score   /5

B Answer all parts of all questions.

1 Fill in the missing letters to reveal words in connection with food chains and webs, then
give a definition of each word.   (4 marks)

  a) ... E R ... I ... ... R E   ....

  b) ... A ... N I ... O ... E   ....

  c) P ... O ... U ... E R   ....

  d) ... O N ... U ... E ...   .

2 Put the links in each of these food chains in the correct order.   (3 marks)

  a) grass, fox, rabbit ....

  b) aphid, rose bush, ladybird ....

  c) field mouse, owl, grasshopper, grass ....

Score   /7

C

These are SATs-style questions. Answer all parts of all questions.

1 A typical woodland food chain is shown below.

Oak leaves ⟹ vole ⟹ weasel ⟹ fox

a) An insecticide was accidentally blown into the woods by the wind and absorbed by the trees. In the food chain above the fox was found to contain the highest levels of insecticide. Explain why. (2 marks)

....

....

....

....

b) The fox population decreased because of the insecticide in their bodies. What effect did this have on the numbers of: (2 marks)

(i) weasels? ....

(ii) voles? ....

2 The following diagrams show three pyramids of numbers.

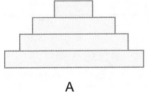   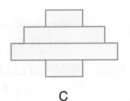

   A   B   C

a) Which of the diagrams A, B or C best represents the food chain: (1 mark)

   Rose bush ⟹ aphids ⟹ ladybirds ⟹ blackbirds

....

b) The aphids began feeding on leaves on the ground. Which diagram best represents the pyramid of numbers now? (1 mark)

....

Score   /6

FOOD CHAINS AND WEBS   Biology

How well did you do?   1–4 **Try again**   5–9 **Getting there**   10–13 **Good work**   14–18 **Excellent!**

For more help on this topic see KS3 Science Success Guide pages 38–39

41

Adaptation and competition

- A habitat is where an organism lives. It has the conditions needed for it to survive.
- A community consists of living things in the habitat.
- Each community is made up of different populations of animals and plants.
- Each population is adapted to live in that particular habitat.

A Choose just one answer, a, b, c or d.

1 Which of the following do animals not compete for? (1 mark)
a) mates   b) space
c) food   d) light

2 Which of the following do plants not compete for? (1 mark)
a) space   b) light
c) food   d) water

3 Which of these is an adaptation of a polar bear?
a) it has a thick coat   (1 mark)
b) it produces little urine
c) it does not sweat
d) it can store water

4 Which of the following allows a camel to survive in the desert? (1 mark)
a) it has a thick coat
b) it can store water
c) it is a good swimmer
d) it is white for camouflage

5 What determines whether an individual animal or a plant can survive? (1 mark)
a) whether it can eat the most
b) whether it is adapted to its environment
c) whether it is tall
d) whether it is large

Score   /5

B Answer all parts of all questions.

1 Draw lines to match the animals and plants with their habitats. (5 marks)

a) frog   path
b) squirrel   rocky shore
c) crab   pond
d) dandelion   river
e) trout   woodland

2 Look at this picture of a cactus; describe three ways in which the cactus has adapted to survive in the desert. (3 marks)

....

....

3 In the same garden two rose bushes were planted close together and one rose bush was planted on its own. Why did the rose bush on its own grow bushier and produce more flowers? (2 marks)

....

....

Score   /10

C This is a SATs-style question. Answer all parts of the question.

1 Hedgehogs hibernate in winter and go into a deep sleep.

a) During the summer, hedgehogs eat a lot and build up a layer of fat under their skin. Give two reasons why this layer of fat is important in the winter.   (2 marks)

   ....

   ....

b) During hibernation the hedgehog's body temperature falls. What is the advantage of this?   (1 mark)

   ....

c) Occasionally, hedgehogs awaken early from their winter sleep. Suggest what could happen if the hedgehogs wake up too early and why this could be a problem.   (2 marks)

   ....

   ....

d) Give the name of another animal that hibernates in the winter.   (1 mark)

   ....

e) Some birds are able to survive the winter by flying to warmer countries. What is this process called?   (1 mark)

   ....

2 Populations do not continue increasing in size forever. Name two factors that stop a population growing.   (2 marks)

   ....

   ....

Score   /9

How well did you do?   1–4 **Try again**   5–9 **Getting there**   10–16 **Good work**   17–24 **Excellent!**

Rocks

There are three types of rock – igneous, sedimentary and metamorphic. Igneous rocks include granite and basalt. Sedimentary rocks include limestone and sandstone. Metamorphic rocks include schist and gneiss.

A Choose just one answer, a, b, c or d.

1 Sedimentary rocks are formed in: **(1 mark)**
a) volcanoes
b) deserts
c) seas and lakes
d) glaciers

2 Which type of rock is formed when molten rock cools and solidifies? **(1 mark)**
a) sedimentary
b) igneous
c) metamorphic
d) crystal

3 Which type of rock may contain fossils?
(1 mark)
a) sedimentary
b) igneous
c) metamorphic
d) granite

4 Extrusive igneous rocks formed: **(1 mark)**
a) below the surface of the Earth
b) above the surface of the Earth
c) slowly
d) over millions of years

5 Which of these is an intrusive igneous rock?
(1 mark)
a) limestone
b) basalt
c) sandstone
d) granite

Score /5

B Answer all parts of the questions.

1 True or false? **(5 marks)**

a) Basalt is an igneous rock.

b) Sedimentary rocks may contain fossils.

c) Limestone is a metamorphic rock.

d) Magma cools down and crystallises to form sedimentary rocks.

e) Metamorphic rocks are formed by high temperatures and pressures on existing rocks.

2 Each of these sentences contains a mistake. Rewrite the sentence without the mistake. **(5 marks)**

a) Sedimentary rocks are harder than igneous rocks.

b) At least 5% of any limestone rock is calcium carbonate.

c) Slate is an igneous rock.

d) Metamorphic rocks are formed by low temperatures and pressures on existing rocks.

e) Igneous rocks may have bands of crystals.

Score /10

44

C These are SATs-style questions. Answer all parts of the questions.

1 The cross-section below shows the different rocks that were found in a cliff face.

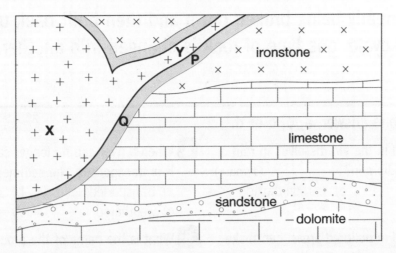

X represents part of a large igneous intrusion and Y represents a smaller igneous intrusion called a sill. Both the rocks found at X and Y contain crystals.

a) Where are the larger crystals found? (1 mark)

....

b) Explain why the crystals are larger at the site you have chosen. (1 mark)

....

c) What type of rock is limestone? (1 mark)

....

d) What type of rock is formed around the outside of the igneous intrusions X and Y? (1 mark)

....

e) Why is the rock formed at Q different to the rock formed at P? (1 mark)

....

f) The rock at Q was originally limestone. What is the name of the rock that it has formed? (1 mark)

....

3 Place these events in order to show the story of how this cliff face was formed. Place the earliest event first. (5 marks)

Limestone is deposited.

Igneous rock intruded.

Sandstone is deposited.

Dolomite is deposited.

Ironstone is deposited.

Score /11

How well did you do? ✗ 1–7 **Try again**   8–12 **Getting there**   13–19 **Good work**   20–26 **Excellent!** ✓

For more information on this topic, see pages 44–45 of your Success Guide.

45

The rock cycle

Rocks are continually being broken down and then built back up again. During the rock cycle, one type of rock is changed into another.

A Choose just one answer, a, b, c or d.

1 Which gas, found in the air, dissolves in rain water to form acidic rain?   (1 mark)
a) oxygen   b) carbon dioxide
c) nitrogen   d) neon

2 Which gas, found in polluted areas, can make rain water even more acidic?   (1 mark)
a) sulphur dioxide   b) oxygen
c) nitrogen   d) neon

3 Pieces of rock are NOT transported by: (1 mark)
a) glaciers   b) rivers and streams
c) granite   d) wind

4 When a river can no longer carry the sediment it is transporting, the sediment is: (1 mark)
a) transported   b) deposited
c) weathered   d) eroded

5 What is the name of the process in which rocks are continually broken down and then reformed into new rocks?   (1 mark)
a) weathering
b) metamorphism
c) the rock cycle
d) transportation

Score   /5

B Answer all parts of the question.

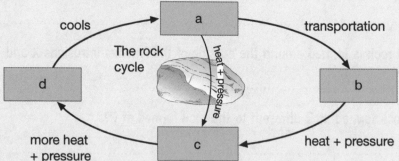

1 a) When molten rock cools it forms .... rocks. Rocks formed slowly below the surface of the Earth are called .... rocks. Those formed more quickly at the Earth's surface in contact with the air or with water are called .... rocks. At the Earth's surface rocks are weathered. Weathering breaks down big rocks into .... pieces. (4 marks)

b) Sedimentary rocks are formed from layers of .... laid down in lakes or seas. As more layers of sediment build up, water is gradually squeezed out of the sediments. Eventually the rock grains become .... together to form sedimentary rocks. These rocks may contain ....   (3 marks)

c) High temperatures and .... can turn existing sedimentary or .... rocks into metamorphic rocks. Examples of .... rocks include schist, gneiss and slate.   (3 marks)

d) When a rock is heated until it melts it forms a liquid called .... When the magma reaches the Earth's surface it is called ....   (2 marks)

Score   /12

C

These are SATs-style questions. Answer all parts of the questions.

1 a) Dolomite is a porous rock. Explain how, in the winter, water can cause the physical weathering of dolomite. *(1 mark)*

....

b) Dolomite reacts with acids. Explain how dolomite can be chemically weathered by rainwater. *(1 mark)*

....

c) A number of events are listed below. Place these events in order to show how granite can be changed into a sedimentary rock. *(6 marks)*

The water is squeezed out of the sediment and the rock grains become cemented together.

Granite is weathered.

The river deposits the sediment.

Layers of sediment build up.

The weathered rock pieces are transported by rivers.

The river flows more slowly as it reaches the sea.

1st event .... 2nd event ....

3rd event .... 4th event ....

5th event .... 6th event ....

2 The diagram below shows two grains taken from the sediment in a riverbed.

a) Describe two differences between grain A and B. *(2 marks)*

....

b) Which grain has been carried furthest by the river? *(1 mark)*

....

A   B

Score /11

How well did you do?   1–7 Try again   8–14 Getting there   15–21 Good work   22–28 Excellent!

For more information on this topic, see pages 44–47 of your Success Guide.   47

Pollution

The atmosphere around us is very precious. To protect it we need to understand how it may become polluted.

A Choose just one answer, a, b, c or d.

1 Which compound causes acid rain? **(1 mark)**
a) nitrogen
b) sulphur dioxide
c) CFCs
d) sodium chloride

2 For how long has the amount of carbon dioxide in the atmosphere been increasing? **(1 mark)**
a) 100 years
b) 200 years
c) your lifetime
d) since the general election

3 What removes some of the carbon dioxide from the atmosphere? **(1 mark)**
a) good summers
b) acid rain
c) time
d) seawater

4 What is a possible effect of global warming? **(1 mark)**
a) acid rain
b) more volcanoes
c) massive flooding
d) damage to statues

5 How does carbon dioxide cause global warming?
a) the gas traps the heat reaching the Earth from the Sun **(1 mark)**
b) it makes acid rain
c) it destroys the ozone layer
d) it attacks chalk and limestone

Score /5

B Answer all parts of all questions.

1 Complete the passage below. **(5 marks)**

Sulphur is found in some fossil .... Sulphur has the chemical symbol S. When substances burn they react with the .... in the air. The formula for a molecule of oxygen is O_2. The compounds formed are called oxides. When sulphur burns in air it forms .... dioxide. Sulphur dioxide is soluble. This means that it .... in water. If sulphur dioxide is released into the atmosphere it can dissolve in rainwater to form acid .... Normally rainwater is slightly acidic because some carbon dioxide will have dissolved in it. However, if sulphur dioxide is present the pH of the solution is even ....

2 Consider each of the statements below, for each one decide whether it is true or false.

a) Limestone contains at least 50% calcium carbonate. .... (1 mark)

b) Sandstone reacts with hydrochloric acid. .... (1 mark)

c) Rainwater can cause fissures and caves in limestone. .... (1 mark)

d) Lichens are good indicators of air pollution. .... (1 mark)

e) Catalysts can only be used once. .... (1 mark)

f) Most catalytic converters are made of silver. .... (1 mark)

Score /11

C These are SATs-style questions. Answer all parts of the questions.

1 a) Name the gas, found in polluted areas, which causes acid rain. (1 mark)

....

b) How is the gas above formed? (1 mark)

....

....

....

c) Give one effect of acid rain. (1 mark)

....

....

....

2 a) Name the gas associated with global warming. (1 mark)

....

b) Give one possible effect of global warming. (1 mark)

....

....

....

3 a) Where would you find a catalytic converter? (1 mark)

....

....

....

b) What does a catalytic converter do? (1 mark)

....

....

....

Score /7

How well did you do? ✗ 1–7 Try again   8–12 Getting there   13–18 Good work   19–23 Excellent! ✓

For more information on this topic, see pages 45 & 48–49 of your Success Guide.

States of matter

There are three states of matter – solid, liquid and gas.

A Choose just one answer, a, b, c or d.

1 Ice is an example of which state of matter?
a) gas   b) liquid   **(1 mark)**
c) solid   d) steam

2 If 10g of ice is melted, how many grams of liquid water are formed?   **(1 mark)**
a) 10g   b) 7g
c) 11g   d) more than 12g

3 The melting point of bromine is −7°C. The boiling point of bromine is 59°C. At room temperature, in which state is bromine found?
a) gas   b) solid   **(1 mark)**
c) liquid   d) water

4 The melting point of ice is 0 °C. At what temperature does water freeze?   **(1 mark)**
a) 0°C   b) 100°C
c) 10°C   d) 25°C

5 Name the change of state being described: "the movement of the liquid particles overcomes the forces of attraction between the particles"   **(1 mark)**
a) condensing
b) boiling
c) melting
d) freezing

Score   /5

B Answer all parts of all questions.

1 Complete the table below to show the state of each of the elements shown at room temperature (25°C).   **(3 marks)**

Element	Melting point (degrees C)	Boiling point (degrees C)	State at room temperature
Chlorine	−101	−35	
Bromine	−7	59	
Rubidium	39	686	

2 Complete the sentences below.   **(11 marks)**

In a solid the .... are close together. They have fixed positions, but they do ....
When a solid is heated the particles move .... so they take up .... space.

The particles in a .... are quite close together, but they do move relative to each other.
This means that liquids have a fixed .... but not a fixed shape. When a liquid is heated the
particles move around more, so the liquid .... Liquids expand more than .... on heating.

The particles in a .... are far apart and moving very .... in all directions.
A .... will fill any container into which it is placed.

Score   /14

C These are SATs-style questions. Answer all parts of the questions.

1 The table below shows the melting points and boiling points of four elements.

Element	Melting point (°C)	Boiling point (°C)
Manganese	1244	1962
Mercury	−39	357
Xenon	−112	−107
Iodine	114	184

a) Which of the elements shown in the table is a gas at room temperature? (1 mark)

....

b) Which of the elements shown in the table is a liquid at room temperature? (1 mark)

....

If the element manganese is heated it can change from a solid to a liquid and eventually to a gas. In which state is manganese when:

c) the atoms are far apart and moving very quickly in all directions? (1 mark)

....

d) the atoms are very close together and vibrate about fixed positions? (1 mark)

....

e) the atoms are quite close together but able to move past each other? (1 mark)

....

A sample of manganese is heated until it melts.

f) What is the change of state that has taken place? .... to .... (1 mark)

2 The graph below shows the melting curve of manganese.

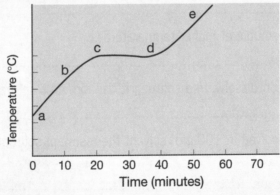

Which letter on the graph shows where the manganese is beginning to change state? (1 mark)

....

Score /7

How well did you do? ✗ 1–7 Try again   8–12 Getting there   13–19 Good work   20–26 Excellent! ✓

For more information on this topic, see pages 50–51 of your Success Guide.

51

Dissolving

If a solid dissolves in a liquid it forms a solution. Even though we can no longer see the solid it is still there, so the overall mass stays the same.

A Choose just one answer, a, b, c or d.

1 If 5 g of a salt dissolves in 100 g of water, what is the mass of the solution? **(1 mark)**
a) 100 g
b) 105 g
c) 5 g
d) 102 g

2 If 0.2 g of a solid dissolves in 100 g of solvent, what is the mass of the solution made? **(1 mark)**
a) 102 g
b) 100.2 g
c) 99.8 g
d) 120 g

3 Which term can be used to describe a solution in which, at a particular temperature, no more solute can be dissolved? **(1 mark)**
a) solvent
b) highly soluble
c) saturated solution
d) disappeared

4 You are given a saturated salt solution. How can you get MORE salt to dissolve? **(1 mark)**
a) evaporate some of the solvent
b) cool the solution
c) let it rest for a few minutes
d) warm the solution

5 What happens to the solubility of most solutes when they are warmed? **(1 mark)**
a) their solubility increases
b) their solubility decreases
c) they have the same solubility
d) they melt more slowly

Score /5

B Answer all parts of the question.

1 Consider the following statements and decide whether each one is true or false.

a) Copper sulphate is insoluble in water **(1 mark)**

....

b) Sugar is more soluble in hot water than in cold water. **(1 mark)**

....

c) Most solutes are more soluble at higher temperatures. **(1 mark)**

....

d) When no more solute can dissolve in a solution it has formed a saturated solution. **(1 mark)**

....

e) If 2 g of a solute is dissolved in 100 g of solvent the resultant solution will have a mass of 102 g. **(1 mark)**

....

f) Water is a solvent for all solids. **(1 mark)**

....

g) If a saturated solution is warmed it can normally dissolve a little more solute. **(1 mark)**

....

Score /7

C This is a SATs-style question. Answer all parts of the question.

1 Harry dissolved some copper sulphate crystals in a beaker of water.

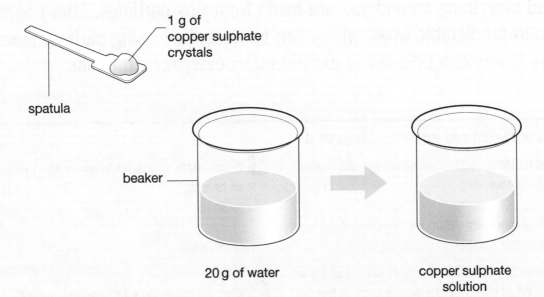

1 g of copper sulphate crystals

spatula

beaker

20 g of water

copper sulphate solution

a) What is the name of the solvent in Harry's experiment? (1 mark)

....

b) What is the name of the solute in Harry's experiment? (1 mark)

....

c) What is the mass of the copper sulphate solution that is made? (1 mark)

....

d) How would Harry know that all the copper sulphate had dissolved? (1 mark)

....

e) How could Harry make the copper sulphate dissolve more quickly? (1 mark)

....

f) Harry adds some copper sulphate crystals to the water until eventually no more crystals will dissolve. What type of solution has been made? (1 mark)

....

g) How could Harry get more copper sulphate to dissolve in the water? (1 mark)

....

Score /7

How well did you do? ✗ 1–5 Try again 6–10 Getting there 11–15 Good work 16–19 Excellent! ✓

For more information on this topic, see pages 52–53 of your Success Guide.

53

Particle theory

You and everything around you are made from tiny particles. These particles behave in predictable ways, which can be described using particle theory. Particle theory can be used to explain many everyday situations.

A Choose just one answer, a, b, c or d.

1 What happens to particles when they are heated?
a) they move less   (1 mark)
b) they get bigger
c) they move around more
d) they get smaller

2 A metal bar is 100 cm long. It is heated for an hour. What could be the new length of the bar?
a) 102 cm   b) 99 cm   (1 mark)
c) 98 cm   d) 99.2 cm

3 Which state of matter expands the MOST on heating?   (1 mark)
a) solid   b) liquid
c) gas   d) metals

4 Which state of matter expands the LEAST on heating?   (1 mark)
a) solid
b) liquid
c) mercury
d) gas

5 Why are there gaps in concrete roads?
(1 mark)
a) to allow for contraction
b) cheaper
c) to allow for expansion
d) it makes it easier to repair one section of the road

Score   /5

B Answer all parts of all questions.

1 Consider the following statements and decide whether each one is true or false.
a) In gases the particles move more slowly than the particles in liquids. .... (1 mark)
b) The particles in gases and liquids can diffuse.   .... (1 mark)
c) The pressure inside a football is caused by the air particles inside the ball crashing into the wall of the football.   .... (1 mark)
d) If a balloon is gently warmed the particles lose energy and begin to move more slowly. .... (1 mark)
e) If an iron bar is heated in an oven the particles in the iron bar become larger. ....(1 mark)

2 Complete the passage below.   (10 marks)

In gases the .... are moving very quickly in all .... A stink bomb can be smelt from the other side of a room because of .... Scent particles from the stink bomb evaporate and turn into a .... These scent particles then bump into .... particles and are eventually spread through the whole room. People close to the stink bomb will smell it first because it takes the scent particles .... time to diffuse through the air to them.

Diffusion also occurs in .... However, in liquids, although the .... are able to move relative to each other, they are not moving as fast as the particles in .... This means that liquids can diffuse, but they do so more slowly than the particles in ....

Score   /15

C This is a SATs-style question. Answer all parts of the question.

1 Oliver pumps up his football.

a) Explain how the gas particles inside the football cause pressure to be exerted on the walls of the football. (1 mark)

....

b) Oliver notices that as he pumps up his football it feels slightly warmer.

Explain how the motion of air particles changed as the football became warmer. (1 mark)

....

c) If Oliver places the football in a fridge, the air inside the ball becomes colder and the pressure inside the football changes.

i) Explain what happens to the pressure inside the football as the air particles get colder. (1 mark)

....

ii) Explain why the change in pressure occurs when the ball is cooled, in terms of the movement of air particles. (1 mark)

....

Score   /4

How well did you do? ✗ 1–6 **Try again** 7–12 **Getting there** 13–18 **Good work** 19–24 **Excellent!** ✓

For more information on this topic, see pages 54–55 of your Success Guide.

55

Atoms and elements

Everything is made up of atoms. Atoms are extremely small. All atoms of the same element have an identical number of protons.

A Choose just one answer, a, b, c or d.

1 How are the elements arranged in the periodic table? **(1 mark)**
a) increasing mass number
b) increasing atomic number
c) colour
d) alphabetically

2 Roughly how many elements are there? **(1 mark)**
a) 100   b) 50
c) 25   d) 1000

3 What are the vertical columns in the periodic table called? **(1 mark)**
a) groups   b) periods
c) areas   d) lines

4 Which particles are found in shells around a nucleus? **(1 mark)**
a) neutrons
b) protons and electrons
c) protons
d) electrons

5 Which particles may be found in the nucleus of an atom? **(1 mark)**
a) protons and neutrons
b) protons and electrons
c) electrons only
d) neutrons only

Score   /5

B Answer all parts of all questions.

1 Consider the following statements. Decide whether each one is true or false.
a) Elements contain only one type of atom. .... (1 mark)
b) Atoms of gold are the same as atoms of oxygen. .... (1 mark)
c) Compounds are formed when atoms of two or more elements are mixed together. .... (1 mark)
d) Compounds are formed when atoms of two or more elements are joined together. .... (1 mark)
e) The horizontal rows in the periodic table are called periods. .... (1 mark)
f) The vertical columns in the periodic table are called groups. .... (1 mark)
g) The element carbon can be represented by the symbol C. .... (1 mark)
h) The element chromium can be represented by the symbol C. .... (1 mark)
i) Protons have a negative charge. .... (1 mark)
j) Neutrons and protons are found in the nucleus of a carbon atom. .... (1 mark)

2 Rearrange the following anagrams then draw a line to join the word you have found to its correct definition.
(5 marks)

Anagrams	Definitions
moat	The central part of an atom which comprises neutrons and protons.
unclesu	A very small particle with a positive charge.
leertocn	A very small particle with no charge.
unroten	A small piece of matter which was previously thought to be the smallest part of any substance.
potnor	A very small particle with a negative charge.

Score   /15

C These are SATs-style questions. Answer all parts of the questions.

1 Read the information in the box below.

> The elements copper and iron are both shiny solids and good conductors of heat and electricity.
>
> The elements nitrogen and oxygen are gases which do not conduct heat or electricity well.
>
> When copper is burnt in air, it reacts with oxygen to form a black solid called copper oxide.

Use the information in the box to answer the following questions.

a) Name an element which is a metal. (1 mark)

....

b) Name an element which is a non-metal. (1 mark)

....

c) Name a metal which can be made into steel. (1 mark)

....

d) Name a compound. (1 mark)

....

2 The symbol for the element oxygen is O.

a) How many atoms are in an oxygen molecule O_2? (1 mark)

....

Use these three diagrams to answer the questions below.

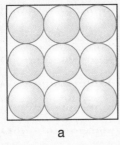 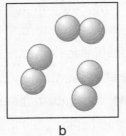 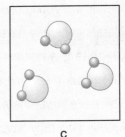

a   b   c

b) Which of these substances is a compound? (1 mark)

....

c) Which of these substances could be oxygen? (1 mark)

....

d) Which two substances are only made of one type of atom? (1 mark)

....

e) What is the name given to substances that only contain one type of atom? (1 mark)

....

Score   /9

How well did you do?   ✗ 1–8 Try again   9–14 Getting there   15–21 Good work   22–29 Excellent! ✓

For more information on this topic, see pages 56–57, 74 & 78 of your Success Guide.

Metals

Three quarters of the elements in the periodic table are metals.

A Choose just one answer, a, b, c or d.

1 Which of these metals is magnetic? (1 mark)
a) gold b) sodium
c) iron d) zinc

2 Which of these metals is a liquid at room temperature? (1 mark)
a) copper b) mercury
c) gold d) zinc

3 Which of these is the only non-metal which conducts electricity? (1 mark)
a) carbon in the form of graphite
b) bromine
c) carbon in the form of diamond
d) mercury

4 Non-metal oxides dissolve in water to form: (1 mark)
a) acidic solutions
b) alkaline solutions
c) neutral solutions
d) chemical reactions

5 Metal oxides dissolve in water to form: (1 mark)
a) neutral solutions
b) acidic solutions
c) alkaline solutions
d) chemical reactions

Score /5

B Answer all parts of all questions.

1 Consider the following statements and decide whether each one is true or false.
a) Metals are good conductors of heat. .... (1 mark)
b) Metals generally have a low density. .... (1 mark)
c) Graphite is a non-metal which conducts electricity. .... (1 mark)
d) All metals are solids at room temperature. .... (1 mark)
e) There are fewer metal than non-metal elements in the periodic table. .... (1 mark)
f) Metals generally have high melting and boiling points.. (1 mark)
g) All non-metal elements are gases at room temperature.. (1 mark)
h) Non-metal elements which are solid at room temperature are brittle
and tend to break when they are hit. .... (1 mark)

2 Complete the following passage. (14 marks)

Most of the elements in the periodic table are .... Metals generally have high melting and .... points, which means that most are .... at room temperature. The only metal that is liquid at room temperature is .... Mercury is used in .... Metals are good conductors of .... Metals have a .... appearance, particularly when the metal is freshly cut. Some metals like iron are ....

Roughly a quarter of the elements in the periodic table are .... - .... These elements have low melting and .... points. Many of these elements are gases, a few are solids and one called .... is liquid. Non-metals are .... conductors of heat and .... The only non-metal element that does conduct electricity is ....

Score /22

C These are SATs-style questions. Answer all parts of the questions.

1 The picture opposite shows a saucepan. The handle is made of a different material from the rest of the saucepan.

a) Use some of these words to complete the sentences below.

boiling point   insulator
conductor   melting point

The saucepan is made of copper. This is because copper is a good .... of heat. Copper also has a very high .... which means that copper does not melt during cooking. **(2 marks)**

b) Suggest one material that the handle of the saucepan could be made from. **(1 mark)**

....

c) What property of the material you have chosen as the handle for the saucepan makes it suitable for this use?
(1 mark)

....

2 These statements are all true of metals.

Metals are good conductors of heat.
Metals are good conductors of electricity.
Metals are shiny.
Metals are strong.

Using only the statements above explain why metals are chosen for the following uses.

a) Gold is used to make necklaces. .... **(1 mark)**

b) Copper is used to make saucepans. .... **(1 mark)**

c) Steel is used to make bridges. .... **(1 mark)**

3

```
        ┌───┐
        │ 1 │
        └───┘                        ┌──────────┐
                                     │        ┌─┤
                                     │      5 │ │
        ┌───┬──────────────┬────────┤   ┌────┘ │
        │   │              │        ├───┤      │
        │ 2 │              │        │   └──┐   │
        │   │      3       │   4    │      │   │
        └───┴──────────────┴────────┴──────┴───┘
```

In which area of the periodic table are the non-metal elements found? ....(1 mark)

Score   /8

How well did you do? ✗ 1–9 Try again   10–19 Getting there   20–27 Good work   28–35 Excellent! ✓

For more information on this topic, see pages 50 & 58–59 of your Success Guide.

59

Unusual elements

Metals and non-metals have characteristic properties. However, there are certain elements which have unexpected properties.

A Choose just one answer, a, b, c or d.

1 Which is the only non-metal element which is a liquid at room temperature? **(1 mark)**
a) chlorine   b) bromine
c) mercury   d) oxygen

2 Which is the only metallic element which is NOT a solid at room temperature? **(1 mark)**
a) bromine   b) lead
c) mercury   d) iron

3 Why is mercury used in thermometers? **(1 mark)**
a) it is cheap
b) solids expand more than liquids on heating
c) it is very dangerous
d) liquids expand more than solids on heating

4 Which pair comprises two forms of carbon? **(1 mark)**
a) diamond and gold
b) graphite and lead
c) graphite and diamond
d) lead and diamond

5 Why does sodium float on water? **(1 mark)**
a) sodium is less dense than water
b) sodium is more dense than water
c) sodium is reactive
d) sodium is a non-metal

Score   /5

B Answer all parts of all questions.

1 Consider the following statements and decide whether each one is true or false.
a) Diamond and graphite are both forms of carbon. .... (1 mark)
b) Bromine is a gas at room temperature. .... (1 mark)
c) Mercury is a solid at room temperature. .... (1 mark)
d) Liquids expand more than solids on heating. .... (1 mark)
e) Sodium is more dense than water, so a lump of sodium will sink in water. .... (1 mark)

2 Metals and non-metals have characteristic properties. **(6 marks)**
Draw lines to connect the metals box and the non-metals box to their characteristic properties. The first two have been done for you.

METALS → high melting points

low density
poor conductors of heat and electricity
shiny
strong
brittle
high density
good conductors of heat and electricity

NON-METALS

Score   /11

C This is a SATs-style question. Answer all parts of the question.

1 The table and diagram below show how four metals reacted with water.

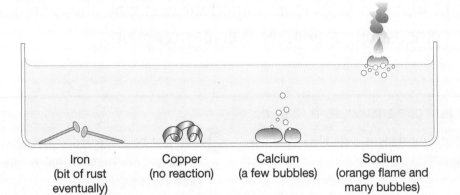

Iron
(bit of rust
eventually)

Copper
(no reaction)

Calcium
(a few bubbles)

Sodium
(orange flame and
many bubbles)

Metal	Reaction when placed in water
iron	very slowly turns brown
copper	no reaction
calcium	a few bubbles are produced
sodium	vigorous reaction, lots of bubbles are produced, sodium burns with an orange flame

a) **Which metal is the most reactive?** (1 mark)

....

b) **Which metal is the least reactive?** (1 mark)

....

c) **Which metal is less dense than water?** (1 mark)

....

d) **What is the gas produced when metals react with water?** (1 mark)

....

e) **Why should sodium NOT be reacted with acids?** (1 mark)

....

Score   /5

How well did you do? ✗ 1–4 **Try again**   5–9 **Getting there**   10–16 **Good work**   17–21 **Excellent!** ✓

For more information on this topic, see pages 58–61 of your Success Guide.

Chemical reactions

The rusting of iron and steel is an important everyday chemical reaction. Burning (or combustion) is another everyday reaction.

A Choose just one answer, a, b, c or d.

1 Which of these substances does NOT stop iron from rusting? **(1 mark)**
a) water
b) paint
c) plastic coating
d) oil

2 Cars are made from steel. The steel is painted. In which of these situations will the steel rust? **(1 mark)**
a) after 3 years
b) when the paint is scratched
c) after 100,000 miles
d) if the car is resprayed a different colour

3 What is the name of the compound formed when magnesium reacts with oxygen? **(1 mark)**
a) magnesium oxygen
b) oxide magnesium
c) magnesium oxide
d) magnesium dioxide

4 Iron can be protected at the expense of a more reactive metal. What is this type of protection called? **(1 mark)**
a) magnesium
b) stainless steel
c) steel
d) sacrificial protection

5 Which of these metals could be used to protect a steel speed boat engine? **(1 mark)**
a) magnesium
b) sodium
c) silver
d) copper

Score /5

B Answer all parts of all questions.

1 Methane has the formula CH_4.
a) Which two elements does methane contain? .... **(2 marks)**
b) Name the two compounds formed when methane is burnt .... **(2 marks)**
c) Write a word equation to describe the burning of methane. .... **(2 marks)**

2 Complete the passage below. **(14 marks)**

The rusting of iron and steel is an important everyday chemical .... Unfortunately it is not a .... reaction, so we try to slow it down or stop it altogether. Steel bike chains can be protected from rusting by coating them with .... The oil prevents the oxygen and .... from reaching the steel, so rusting does not occur.

.... fences can be protected by coating them with plastic, this stops the .... and water from reaching the steel. But if the plastic is damaged the steel will ....

Another method to stop rusting is to mix iron with different metals such as chromium to form the alloy stainless steel. This does not rust but steel produced in this way is more expensive to buy.

Another useful way to protect expensive .... objects is to use sacrificial .... This method could be used to protect speed boat .... A reactive metal like .... or .... is placed next to the steel engine. The more reactive metal reacts instead of the .... Overall the steel is ...., but at the expense of the more reactive metal.

Score /20

62

C   These are SATs-style questions. Answer all parts of the questions.

1 The fuels octane and methane are both hydrocarbons.
Octane has the formula C_8H_{18}.
Methane has the formula CH_4.

a) Give the formulae of the two products formed when methane is burnt.   (2 marks)

....

b) Why does the complete combustion of octane and of methane produce the same products? (1 mark)

....

c) Write a balanced symbol equation to represent the complete combustion of methane.   (2 marks)
.... + ... ➔ .... + ...

2 Sarah placed three new iron nails into test tubes. The labels on the test tubes show what was in each one.

A   B   C

Powdered calcium chloride (a drying agent)   Boiled water (boiling water removes any dissolved gases)   Water

a) After one week Sarah found that only the nail in test tube C had rusted. Explain why the nails did not rust in test tube A and test tube B.   (2 marks)

test tube A ....

test tube B ....

b) Sarah took the nail that had rusted out of test tube C and found its mass using a mass balance. She noticed that the nail's mass had increased. Explain why this happened.   (1 mark)

....

Score   /8

How well did you do?   ✗ 1–9 **Try again**   10–19 **Getting there**   20–27 **Good work**   28–33 **Excellent!** ✓

For more information on this topic, see pages 62–63 of your Success Guide.

63

Reactivity series

Some metals are more reactive than others. The metals can be placed in order of reactivity.

A Choose just one answer, a, b, c or d.

1 Name the compound formed when magnesium is burned. **(1 mark)**
a) calcium oxide
b) magnesium nitride
c) magnesium oxide
d) magnesium carbonate

2 Which of these metals will burn the most fiercely? **(1 mark)**
a) magnesium   b) zinc
c) iron   d) copper

3 What is made when a metal reacts with water? **(1 mark)**
a) metal hydroxide
b) hydrogen
c) metal hydroxide and oxygen
d) metal hydroxide and hydrogen

4 Name the products made when calcium reacts with water. **(1 mark)**
a) calcium carbonate and hydrogen
b) calcium hydroxide and oxygen
c) calcium hydroxide and hydrogen
d) hydrogen only

5 Name the gas produced when metals react with acids. **(1 mark)**
a) hydrogen
b) oxygen
c) carbon dioxide
d) helium

Score /5

Most reactive

Potassium (K)

Sodium (Na)

Calcium (Ca)

Magnesium (Mg)

Zinc (Zn)

Iron (Fe)

Lead (Pb)

Copper (Cu)

Gold (Au)

Least reactive

B Answer all parts of all questions.

1 Complete the following word equations.
a) magnesium + oxygen   → .... (1 mark)
b) iron + oxygen   → .... (1 mark)
c) copper + oxygen   → .... (1 mark)
d) potassium + water   → .... + ... (2 marks)
e) sodium + water   → .... + ... (2 marks)
f) calcium + water   → .... + ... (2 marks)
g) magnesium + hydrochloric acid → .... + ... (2 marks)
h) magnesium + hydrochloric acid → .... + ... (2 marks)
i) calcium + hydrochloric acid → .... + ... (2 marks)
j) zinc + hydrochloric acid   → .... + ... (2 marks)

2 Complete the following symbol equations.
a) $2Mg + O_2 \rightarrow 2$............. (1 mark)
b) $2Fe + O_2 \rightarrow 2$............. (1 mark)
c) $C +$ .... $\rightarrow CO_2$ (1 mark)

Score /20

KS3
Success

**Workbook
Answer
Booklet**

Science
SATs

Levels 5-7

Answers

CELLS

Section A
1 a   2 c
3 b   4 b
5 d

Section B
1 A = chloroplast B = cell wall
  C = vacuole
2 onion cell has nucleus, cell wall, mitochondria, no chloroplasts
  palisade cell has all four
  human skin cell has a nucleus and mitochondria, no chloroplasts or cell wall
  (1 mark for each correct tick and cross)

Section C
1 a) A nucleus
  b) carry oxygen
  c) for strength and support of the plant cell
  d) they contain chlorophyll that absorbs sunlight for photosynthesis
  e) palisade cells and root hair cells
2 a) sperm cell, egg cell, nerve cell

ORGAN SYSTEMS

Section A
1 b   2 d
3 d   4 c
5 c

Section B
1 A = flower, contains the reproductive organs
  B = stem, holds the plant upright or/and contains the xylem and phloem tubes
  C = root, anchors the plant in the soil
  D = leaf, carries out photosynthesis
2 xylem tubes carry water and nutrients
  phloem tubes carry glucose

Section C
1 a) excretory system (accept excretion)
  b) bladder
2 a) nervous system
  b via nerves/nerve cells
  c) any of the other organ systems, named = 1 mark, organs = 1 mark, function = 1 mark:
  circulatory – heart and blood vessels, digestive – oesophagus, stomach, etc, muscular – muscles, reproductive – testes, ovaries, etc, respiratory – lungs, etc, skeletal – bones

NUTRITION & FOOD TESTS

Section A
1 a   2 a
3 d   4 b
5 c

Section B
1 carbohydrates, fats, protein, vitamins and minerals (any order)
  carbohydrates, starch, repair, store, iodine, blue/black, heat, orange, Biuret, purple, constipation

Section C
1 a) carbohydrates, fats.
  b) he has a more active job (accept he uses up more energy, do not accept he works harder or has a tougher job or does hard work)
  c) for growth and repair of cells (accept to repair our bodies or for growth)
  d) a pregnant female has to supply both the baby and herself with protein
  e) boys tend to be larger/bigger at that age
  f) One may be more active/plays sport or works harder

THE DIGESTIVE SYSTEM

Section A
1 b   2 c
3 a   4 d
5 b

Section B
1 a) proteases, amino acids
  b) carbohydrases, glucose
  c) lipases, fatty acids and glycerol
2 correct words – large, insoluble, small, soluble
3 mouth, oesophagus, stomach, small intestine

Section C
1 a) the protein/egg white had been digested/broken down
  b) an enzyme (accept chemical)
  c) stops it working/ denatures the enzyme
  d) it's the temperature of the body/to mimic body conditions of digestion
  e) digestion of protein needs an enzyme (1 mark), the correct temperature and acidic conditions (either one)
2 a) the stomach
  b) amino acids

THE HEART

Section A
1 b   2 d
3 b   4 c
5 c

Section B
1 **vein** – carries blood towards the heart at low pressure, contains valves
  artery – carries blood away from the heart at high pressure, has thick walls.

  capillary – carries deoxygenated and oxygenated blood, has very thin walls
2 false, true, true, false, false, true

Section C
1 a) to pump blood around the body
  b) arteries
  c) pulmonary artery
  d) the left
2 a) an artery has thicker walls, elasticated walls, a smaller lumen, has no valves (or converse argument with veins)
  b) capillaries

BLOOD AND CIRCULATION

Section A
1 d   2 b
3 a   4 a
5 d

Section B
1 red blood cells
2 A = red blood cells, carry oxygen B = white blood cells, fight infection/disease C = platelets, clot blood
3 the blood passes through the heart twice; the two pathways are heart – lungs – heart and heart – body – heart

Section C
1 a) the athlete is able to get more oxygen (1 mark) to his/her muscles/cells (1 mark)
  b) haemoglobin
2 a) pulmonary artery – lungs – pulmonary vein – heart
  b) carbon dioxide
  c) plasma
  d) soluble food, salts, carbon dioxide, urea, hormones, antibodies, plasma proteins (any one)

MOVEMENT

Section A
1 a   2 b
3 c   4 c
5 d

Section B
1 joint, muscles, cartilage, tendons, ligaments, biceps, triceps, central nervous system.
2 support, protection, and movement
3 reflex action

Section C
1 a) the bones will rub/hit against each other and become worn, less movement will be possible, inflammation or swelling, there will be no friction at the joint (any two)
  b) ligaments
  c) muscles
2 a) biceps and triceps
  b) biceps
  c) triceps

THE LUNGS & BREATHING

Section A
1 b   2 c
3 b   4 a
5 d

Section B
1 a) alveolus
  b) bronchiole
  c) gas exchange
  d) carbon dioxide and oxygen
  e) any one from moist membrane, millions of them (surface area), close contact with blood capillaries
2 the correct words are: contract, up, out, increases

Section C
1 a) trachea, bronchi, bronchioles, alveoli
  b) the alveoli/air sacs
  c) oxygen
  d) carbon dioxide
2 a) glucose/sugar
  b) in the cells/cytoplasm/mitochondria
  c) for growth, building up the body, storage, making fat, keeping warm, active transport (any one)

PUBERTY & REPRODUCTION

Section A
1 c   2 d
3 a   4 b
5 b

Section B
1 male: A = bladder B = sperm duct C = penis D = urethra E = scrotum F = testes/testicle G = glands
  female: A = Fallopian tube B = ovary C = uterus D = cervix E = vagina F = uterus lining

Section C
1 a) the placenta prevents some harmful substances from reaching the baby and the amniotic fluid cushions/protects the baby from knocks/bumps and supports the baby
  b) the umbilical cord and placenta
  c) they contract
2 a) the ovaries or ovary
  b) body hair or pubic hair or hairy armpits, growth of breasts, growth spurt, menstruation begins, skin becomes more oily (do not accept grows taller) (any one change)

DRUGS

Section A
1 c   2 a
3 b   4 c
5 d

Section B
1 alcohol, cigarette, hallucinogen, sedative, stimulant, painkiller, solvent.

Section C

1. a) tar
   b) cancer
   c) carbon monoxide (accept carbon dioxide)
   d) nicotine – causes addiction and is a mild stimulant
2. a) cirrhosis
   b) depressant

FIGHTING DISEASE

Section A
1 d   2 b
3 b   4 c
5 c

Section B
1. a) broken skin; respiratory, reproductive and digestive systems; eyes, ears (any three)
   b) produce antitoxins, antibodies or engulf the microbes (any two)
2. a) vaccines
   b) antibiotics (accept named antibiotic or antiseptic)
3. fungi and viruses
4. tetanus, chicken pox, tuberculosis, measles

Section C
1. a) they both have no nucleus
   b) a virus is much smaller and it has a protein coat, not a cell wall or cell membrane (any one)
   c) vaccines contain weakened viruses (1 mark), the body then makes antibodies/antitoxins to destroy the new healthy virus (1 mark)
2. a) 37°C
   b) keep the lid on the dish/seal/secure the dish, wear gloves/a mask/goggles (any two)

PHOTOSYNTHESIS

Section A
1 a   2 c
3 d   4 d
5 a

Section B
1. nitrate – stunted growth and yellow older leaves
   phosphate – poor root growth and purple young leaves
   potassium – yellow leaves with dead spots
2. a) palisade cells
   b) stoma
   c) waterproof layer
   d) leaf vein

Section C
1. a) oxygen
   b) test with a glowing splint, the splint should relight
   c) plenty of light, carbon dioxide and the correct temperature
   d) glucose (accept starch or sugar)
2. a) blue/black
   b) starch

PLANT REPRODUCTION

Section A
1 b   2 c
3 b   4 d
5 a

Section B
1. filament = male
   style = female
   stigma = female, receives the pollen grains
   ovary = female, contains ovules, once fertilised turns into a fruit
   anther = male, produces pollen
2. tomato – seeds dispersed by animals eating them and then producing droppings that contain the seeds
   dandelion – wind (accept stuck to animals)
   sweet pea – popping out (accept animals eat them)

Section C
1. a) the pollen from an anther landing on a stigma
   b) stigmas are large and hang out of the flower so they can catch pollen, anthers are also outside the flower and exposed, anthers have long filaments (any two)
   c) brightly coloured, it has a scent, it contains sweet nectar (any two)

CARBON & NITROGEN CYCLES

Section A
1 a   2 c
3 d   4 b
5 c

Section B
1. a) 1 = 0.03% 2 = photosynthesis
      3 = eating 4 = decomposers
      5 = respiration 6 = fossils
      7 = burned

Section C
1. a) 1. bacteria in the soil and in root nodules of plants convert nitrogen in air into nitrates
      2. plants take up the nitrates from the soil and convert them into proteins
      3. animals eat plants to take protein into their bodies and use to make their own protein
      4. animals and plants produce waste and die; bacteria release the nitrogen in the waste and bodies back into the soil
      5. bacteria can convert nitrates back into nitrogen gas
   b) for making proteins
   c) waterlogged soil with little or no oxygen

CLASSIFICATION

Section A
1 c   2 a
3 b   4 c
5 d

Section B
1. A = sycamore B = privet
   C = silver birch D = oak
2. a) snail
   b) millipede
   c) daisy

Section C
1. a) vertebrates
   b) invertebrates
2. a) any reasonable example of an animal belonging to each group (1 mark each)
   characteristics (any one) (1 mark)
   i) fish – live in water, have scales and fins, breathe though gills
   ii) mammals – give birth to live young, have hair, feed young on milk, warm-blooded
   iii) birds – have feathers and wings, lay eggs, most can fly
   iv) reptiles – have dry scaly skin, most live on land
   v) amphibians – have smooth moist skin, live on land and in water, breed in water

VARIATION

Section A
1 d   2 d
3 b   4 a
5 c

Section B
1. A = continuous
   B = discontinuous
2. height = continuous
   hair colour = discontinuous
   blood group = discontinuous
   weight = continuous
   foot size = continuous
   eye colour = discontinuous
   finger length = continuous
3. their environment or how they are brought up will affect what they look like

Section C
1. a) they have inherited different genes/characteristics/DNA
   b) selective breeding
   c) hair, aggression, lack of meat, tusks (any two)
   d) lack of hair, quietness, fatter, less aggressive (any two)

INHERITANCE AND GENETICS

Section A
1 a   2 d
3 c   4 c
5 b

Section B
1. chromosomes, pairs, genes, DNA, dominant, recessive, mutation, radiation
2. a) Red
   b) Rr
   c) R r
      R RR Rr
      r Rr rr   3 : 1 red to white

Section C
1. a) the environment/how we are brought up
   b) the nucleus (accept chromosomes)
   c) 46
   d) 20
2. a) 2
   b) 2
   c) Bb

FOOD CHAINS & WEBS

Section A
1 c   2 a
3 c   4 d
5 b

Section B
1. a) herbivore – an animal that eats only plant material
   b) carnivore – an animal that eats meat
   c) producer – a plant that produces its own food by photosynthesis
   d) consumer – an animal that eats other animals, or plants
2. a) grass ⇨ rabbit ⇨ fox
   b) rose bush ⇨ aphid ⇨ ladybird
   c) grass ⇨ grasshopper ⇨ field mouse ⇨ owl

Section C
1. a) the fox eats the weasels which contain insecticide, the weasels eat the voles which contain insecticide from the oak leaves; the fox eats a lot of weasels or the weasels eat a lot of voles, (answers should imply that the level of insecticide gets more concentrated)
   b) i) weasels would increase (at first)
      ii) voles would decrease (at first)
2. a) C
   b) A

ADAPTATION & COMPETITION

Section A
1 d   2 c
3 a   4 b
5 b

Section B
1. a) frog–pond
   b) squirrel–woodland
   c) crab–rocky shore
   d) dandelion–path
   e) trout–river
2. a cactus has no leaves, it has spines instead to reduce water loss, the spines also protect against being eaten/a cactus is able to store water in its thick stem for periods when there is no rainfall/a cactus root system is very well developed to search out water over a large area and the roots are also very strong to anchor the cactus in the sand (any three points)
3. the rose bush on its own had no competition for water, nutrients and light so was able to grow well (1 mark for competition, second mark if other words in bold are mentioned) (accept just one)

Section C
1. a) fat is a good source/store of energy and it insulates/keeps the heat in the body (Not a good food source)
   b) reduced heat loss, less energy needed, fat lasts longer
   c) food would be in short supply/no food and they would be cold and lose too much heat
   d) dormice, ladybirds, squirrels, frogs etc. (any reasonable answer)
   e) migration

3

2 a) disease, predators, lack of water or food, climate, competition, human activity (any two)

ROCKS

Section A
1 c   2 a
3 a   4 b
5 d

Section B
1 a) true
  b) true
  c) false
  d) false
  e) true
2 a) Sedimentary rocks are softer than igneous rocks.
  b) At least 50% of any limestone rock is calcium carbonate.
  c) Slate is a metamorphic rock.
  d) Metamorphic rocks are formed by high temperatures and pressures on existing rocks.
  e) Metamorphic rocks may have bands of crystals.

Section C
1 a) x
  b) x is a larger intrusion, so the crystals formed more slowly, resulting in larger crystals
  c) sedimentary
  d) metamorphic
  e) it is formed from a different sedimentary rock
  f) marble
2 Dolomite is deposited.
  Sandstone is deposited.
  Limestone is deposited.
  Ironstone is deposited.
  Igneous rock intruded.

THE ROCK CYCLE

Section A
1 b   2 a
3 c   4 b
5 c

Section B
1 a) igneous, intrusive igneous, extrusive igneous, smaller
  b) sediment, cemented, fossils
  c) pressures, igneous, metamorphic
  d) magma, lava

Section C
1 a) as dolomite is porous, water can get into the gaps between grains, as this freezes to form ice it expands and this process can eventually break up the rock.
  b) when carbon dioxide in the air dissolves in rain water it forms a slightly acidic solution, this acidic rain can then react with the dolomite, slowly dissolving it away.
  c) **1st event** Granite is weathered.
    2nd event The weathered rock pieces are transported by rivers.
    3rd event The river flows more slowly as it reaches the sea.
    4th event The river

deposits the sediment.
    5th event Layers of sediment build up
    6th event The water is squeezed out of the sediment and the rock grains become cemented together.
2 a) grain A is larger, jagged and sharp
  b) grain B has been carried further

POLLUTION

Section A
1 b   2 b
3 d   4 c
5 a

Section B
1 fuels, oxygen, sulphur, dissolves, rain, lower
2 a) true   b) false
  c) true   d) true
  e) false   f) false

Section C
1 a) sulphur dioxide
  b) many fossil fuels contain a little sulphur, when these are burnt the sulphur present can form sulphur dioxide
  c) damage to trees/buildings/ statues/lakes etc
2 a) carbon dioxide (accept methane)
  b) ice caps melt/flooding of low level areas/disruption of normal weather patterns
3 a) car exhaust
  b) convert harmful pollutants like carbon monoxide, unburnt hydrocarbons and nitrogen oxides into carbon dioxide, water and nitrogen

STATES OF MATTER

Section A
1 c   2 a
3 c   4 a
5 b

Section B
1 chlorine–gas
  bromine–liquid
  rubidium–solid
2 particles, vibrate, more, move, liquid, volume, expands, solids, gas, fast/quickly, gas

Section C
1 a) xenon
  b) mercury
  c) gas
  d) solid
  e) liquid
  f) solid to liquid
2 c

DISSOLVING

Section A
1 b   2 b
3 c   4 d
5 a

Section B
1 a) false   b) true
  c) true   d) true
  e) true   f) false
  g) true

Section C
1 a) water
  b) copper sulphate
  c) 21g
  d) he can no longer see the solid
  e) he could warm the water/stir it
  f) saturated solution
  g) he could warm the solution, so that the solution is no longer saturated and can dissolve a little more solid

PARTICLE THEORY

Section A
1 c   2 a
3 c   4 a
5 c

Section B
1 a) false   b) true
  c) true   d) false
  e) false
2 particles, directions, diffusion, gas, air, less, liquids, particles, gases, gases

Section C
1 a) the gas particles are moving quickly in all directions, this means that they are continually colliding with the walls of the football, causing pressure to be exerted
  b) they moved faster
  c) i) decrease/get less
    ii) the air particles have less energy, so move more slowly, they collide with the walls of the football less often and with less energy, so the pressure decreases

ATOMS AND ELEMENTS

Section A
1 b   2 d
3 a   4 d
5 a

Section B
1 a) true   b) false
  c) false   d) true
  e) true   f) true
  g) true   h) false
  i) false   j) true
2 **atom** – a small piece of matter which was previously thought to be the smallest part of any substance
  nucleus – the central part of an atom which comprises neutrons and protons
  electron – a very small particle with a negative charge
  neutron – a very small particle with no charge
  proton – a very small particle with a positive charge

Section C
1 a) copper/iron
  b) nitrogen/oxygen
  c) iron
  d) copper oxide
2 a) 2
  b) C
  c) B
  d) A and B
  e) element

METALS

Section A
1 c   2 b
3 a   4 a
5 c

Section B
1 a) true   b) false
  c) true   d) false
  e) false   f) true
  g) false   h) true
2 metals, boiling, solids, mercury, thermometers, heat/electricity, shiny, magnetic, non-metals, boiling, bromine, poor, electricity, carbon (graphite)

Section C
1 a) conductor, melting point
  b) wood/plastic
  c) it should be a good insulator/poor conductor of heat
2 a) metals are shiny
  b) metals are good conductors of heat.
  c) metals are strong.
3 Area 5

UNUSUAL ELEMENTS

Section A
1 b   2 c
3 d   4 c
5 a

Section B
1 a) true   b) false
  c) false   d) true
  e) false
2 **metals**
  shiny
  strong
  high density
  good conductors of heat and electricity
  non-metals
  poor conductors of heat and electricity
  brittle

Section C
a) sodium
b) copper
c) sodium
d) hydrogen
e) sodium is too reactive/dangerous

CHEMICAL REACTIONS

Section A
1 a   2 b
3 c   4 d
5 a

Section B
1 a) carbon and hydrogen
  b) water vapour and carbon dioxide
  c) methane + oxygen ⇒ carbon dioxide + water vapour
2 reaction, useful, oil, water, steel/iron, air/oxygen, rust, steel, protection, engines, magnesium, zinc, steel, protected

Section C
1 a) CO_2 and H_2O
  b) They are both made of the same elements (carbon and hydrogen)
  c) $CH_4 + 2O_2 \Rightarrow 2H_2O + CO_2$

c) $CH_4 + 2O_2 \Rightarrow 2H_2O + CO_2$

2 a) test tube a – no water, test tube b – no air (oxygen)
  b) It has combined with oxygen (which has mass) to form rust

REACTIVITY SERIES

Section A
1 c 2 a
3 d 4 c
5 a

Section B
1 a) magnesium oxide
  b) iron oxide
  c) copper oxide
  d) potassium hydroxide + hydrogen
  e) sodium hydroxide + hydrogen
  f) calcium hydroxide + hydrogen
  g) magnesium chloride + hydrogen
  h) magnesium chloride + hydrogen
  i) calcium chloride + hydrogen
  j) zinc chloride + hydrogen
2 a) MgO b) FeO
  c) O_2 d) H_2O
  e) H_2 f) H_2

Section C
1 a) sodium, magnesium, zinc, silver
  b) hydrogen
  c) magnesium chloride
  d) i) gold/copper
    ii) potassium/calcium
2 a) calcium/hydrogen
  b) potassium/sodium
  c) magnesium/zinc/iron/ lead/copper/gold

DISPLACEMENT REACTIONS

Section A
1 b 2 c
3 b 4 b
5 a

Section B
1 a) i) yes
    ii) no
    iii) yes
    iv) no
    v) no
  b) i) calcium oxide + iron
    ii) iron oxide + copper
    iii) calcium oxide + magnesium
    iv) magnesium oxide + copper
    v) magnesium oxide + iron
  c) i) $ZnSO_4$
    ii) $CuSO_4$
    iii) Cu
    iv) $MgSO_4 + Fe$
    v) $FeSO_4 + Cu$

Section C
1 a) copper/magnesium sulphate ✗
    copper/zinc sulphate ✗
    magnesium/iron sulphate ✓
    iron/copper sulphate ✓
  b) magnesium, zinc, iron, copper
  c) magnesium, shinium, zinc, iron, copper
  d) i) copper
    ii) magnesium + iron sulphate ⇒ magnesium sulphate + iron
  e) $Mg + FeSO_4 \Rightarrow MgSO_4 + Fe$

ACIDS AND ALKALIS

Section A
1 c 2 b
3 b 4 c
5 b

Section B
1 7, neutral, 1, 6, alkalis, 8, acids, alkalis, sour/bitter, indicators, colour, Indicator, acidic, alkaline, acids, orange, yellow, alkalis, purple, alkalis, goggles

Section C
1 a) Shimmer and Shine
  b) Shine-a-Lot
  c) weakly acidic
  d) orange
  e) blue
2 a) potato
  b) lime

MAKING SALTS

Section A
1 d 2 d
3 c 4 a
5 c

Section B
1 b) e) c) a) d)
2 a) hydrogen
  b) magnesium
  c) copper sulphate
  d) carbon dioxide + water
  e) water
  f) sulphuric acid

Section C
1 a) copper chloride + water + carbon dioxide
  b) i) $CuSO_4 + H_2O$
    ii) $CuSO_4 + H_2O + CO_2$
  c) i) 2
    ii) 1
    iii) 4
    iv) 7

CHEMICAL TESTS

Section A
1 a 2 b
3 c 4 a
5 c

Section B
1 carbon dioxide, bubbled, milky/cloudy, lighted, "squeaky pop", oxygen, air, glowing, relights
2 a) oxygen
  b) hydrogen
  c) carbon dioxide
  d) hydrogen
  e) carbon dioxide
  f) oxygen

Section C
1

Highly flammable

Corrosive

Toxic

Harmful h

2 a) oxygen
  b) carbon dioxide

MIXTURES

Section A
1 b 2 a
3 a 4 c
5 b

Section B
1 **mixtures** – butter, seawater, granite, air
  pure compounds – silicon dioxide, sodium chloride, water
  pure elements – neon, oxygen
2 mixture, nitrogen, N, oxygen, element, O_2, carbon, vapour, neon, argon, minerals, compound, quartz, minerals

Section C
1 a) neon
  b) argon
  c) gas to solid
2 a) D
  b) E
  c)

(mixed together)

SEPARATION TECHNIQUES

Section A
1 c 2 a
3 b 4 d
5 a

Section B
1 salt from salty water – evaporation
  the colours in fountain pen ink – chromatography
  iron from iron filings and sand – magnet
  water from alcohol and water – fractional distillation
  mud from muddy water – filtering
2 a) true b) false
  c) true d) false
  e) false f) true
  g) true

Section C
1 a) chromatography
  b) "B" or green
  c) i) red, purple and yellow
    ii) blue and red

COMPOUNDS

Section A
1 c 2 b
3 d 4 a
5 a

Section B
1 **compound** – a substance made of atoms of 2 or more elements that have been chemically joined together
  property – a quality which is always present in a substance, however much of it is present
  molecule – a small piece of a substance which has all the properties of a substance
  magnet – a substance which does, or can attract other materials
  reaction – a chemical change
2 atom, molecules, compound, reactions, products, reactants, iron sulphide, metal, yellow, iron sulphide

Section C
1 a) bubbles/fizzing or temperature increase/ decrease in mass
2 a) i) carbon dioxide gas escapes or carbon dioxide has mass
    ii) hydrochloric acid or magnesium carbonate
  b) C

NAMING COMPOUNDS

Section A
1 b 2 d
3 a 4 a
5 d

Section B
1 a) oxygen
  b) sulphur
  c) copper oxide
  d) sodium fluoride
  e) chlorine
  f) oxygen
  g) potassium iodide
  h) zinc
  i) oxygen
  j) oxygen
2 a) potassium hydroxide
  b) magnesium carbonate
  c) iron sulphate
  d) calcium oxide
  e) potassium chloride

Section C
1 a) i) sodium chloride
    ii) potassium chloride
  b) i) 3
    ii) 4
    iii) 6
2 b) and c)

BALANCING EQUATIONS

Section A
1 a 2 a
3 b 4 b
5 a

Section B
1 a) i) 1
    ii) 1
    iii) 3
  b) i) 1
    ii) 1
    iii) 4
  c) i) 6
    ii) 14
2 a) $H_2 + I_2 \Rightarrow 2HI$
  b) $H_2 + Cl_2 \Rightarrow 2HCl$
  c) $2H_2 + O_2 \Rightarrow 2H_2O$
  d) $Mg + 2HCl \Rightarrow MgCl_2 + H_2$
  e) $Zn + H_2SO_4 \Rightarrow ZnSO_4 + H_2$

Section C
1 a) sodium is too reactive to be reacted directly with sulphuric acid/too dangerous
  b) i) 2
    ii) 1
    iii) 4
    iv) 7
  c) $2NaOH + H_2SO_4 \Rightarrow Na_2SO_4 + 2H_2O$
2 a) copper oxide
  b) $2Cu + O_2 \Rightarrow 2CuO$

SPEED

Section A
1 d 2 a
3 b 4 c
5 c

Section B
1 a) 25 m/s

b) 100 m/s,
c) 200 km/h
2 a) 1000 m
   b) 900 m
   c) 3600 m
3 a) 50 s
   b) 200 s
   c) 2.5 h
4 the skier
5 the aircraft
6 the pilot

Section C
1 a) metre rule and timer
   b) the angle of the ramp, the distance over which the speed of the trolley is to be measured, the way in which the trolley is released, etc.
   c) the greater the angle the greater the average speed
   d) 12.5 m/s
   e) make himself more streamlined, give himself a push start at the top of the slope, etc

GRAPHS OF MOTION

Section A
1 d   2 c
3 b   4 a
5 a

Section B
1 a) BC   b) 125 s
   c) AB   d) 4 m/s
   e) 1000 m   f) 2 m/s

Section C
1 a) CD   b) 0.5 h
   c) EF   d) 90 km/h
   e) 120 km (i.e. total distance = 60 × 0.5 + 90 × 1.0 = 120km)
   f) 60 km/h
2 a)

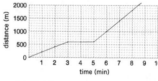

   b) 2 min
   c) 5–8 min
   d) 400 m/min
   e) 225 m/min

FORCES

Section A
1 c   2 c
3 a   4 d
5 d

Section B
1 **Balanced** These forces will have no effect on the motion of an object.
   Newton This is the unit we use to measure forces.
   Upthrust A force exerted upon an object placed in a liquid.
   Unbalanced These forces will change the motion of an object.
   Newtonmeter An instrument for measuring the size of a force.
   Weight The gravitational force that pulls an object downwards.
   Magnet This object can apply forces to other objects without being in contact.

---

2 a) D   b) A   c) C
   d) air resistance and friction on skates

Section C
1 a) and b)

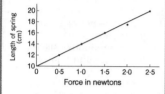

   c) 2.0 N, 17.5 cm,
   d) 13.0 cm
   e) 1.25 N
   f) 2.0 cm

FRICTION AND TERMINAL VELOCITY

Section A
1 b   2 b
3 a   4 a
5 d

Section B
1 start, spikes, speed, streamlined, frictional, air, ice, lubricant, wax, streamlined
2 a) rock climbing, tug of war, etc
   b) swimming, speed skating, cycling, etc

Section C
1 a) gravity
   b) it increases
   c) air resistance or drag
   d) they are balanced
   e) air resistance is now greater than the gravitational forces pulling her downwards
2 a) the surfaces of the blocks will become worn and warm
   b) axle of wheels, on chain or cogs, etc

MOMENTS

Section A
1 c   2 d
3 d   4 b
5 a

Section B
1 a) 4 Nm
   b) 20 Nm
2 a) 15 Nm
   b) 35 Nm
   c) 10 Nm
3 A turn anticlockwise
   B turn clockwise
   C balance
   D turn anticlockwise
   E turn clockwise
   F balanced

Section C
1 a) the moment created by the crate is greater than the moment created by the girl
   b) move further back from the centre of the plank
   c) by moving further away from the centre of the plank she increases the moment created by her weight until it is equal to the moment created by the large crate

---

2 a)

Force in newtons	Distance from pivot (cm)	Anticlockwise moment (Ncm)	Force in newtons	Distance from pivot (cm)	Clockwise moment (Ncm)
4	20	80	5	16	80
10	40	400	20	20	400
5	18	90	3	30	90
8	30	240	5	50	250
6	50	300	10	30	300

   b) the fourth set of results did not fit the pattern
   c) the beam balances when the clockwise moments and the anti-clockwise moments are equal

PRESSURE

Section A
1 c   2 c
3 b   4 b
5 b

Section B
1 a) false   b) true   c) false
   d) true   e) false f) false
   g) true
2 a) 2 Pa   b) 5 Pa   c) 10 Pa
3 a) 30 N   b) 20 N   c) 24 N

Section C
1 a) 300 Pa b) 100 Pa
   c) 200 Pa d) B
2

LIGHT RAYS & REFLECTION

Section A
1 c   2 b
3 c   4 d
5 d

Section B
1 transparent, opaque, opaque, shadow, fire or star or lamp, luminous, non-luminous, light, shape, light, straight lines, faster, hear, thunder
2

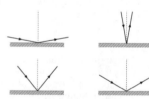

Section C
1 a) light or lamp or bulb
   b) boy, girl, door, wall, etc
   c) because she is wearing a blindfold no light can enter her eyes
   d)

2 a) 2 m   b) 1.5 m
   c) his left appears on the right of his image, etc

REFRACTION & COLOUR

Section A
1 a   2 a
3 d   4 d
5 c

Section B
1 a) white light hits the red ball, all the colours are absorbed except for red which is reflected into the eye of the observer, so the ball appears red
   b) white light hits the blue box, all the colours are absorbed except for blue which is reflected into the eye of the observer, so the box appears blue
   c) white light hits the white sheet of paper, none of the colours are absorbed, they are all reflected, so the paper appears white
   d) white light hits the black cat, all the colours are absorbed, none are reflected into the eye of the observer, so the cat appears black
2 a) the change in direction of a ray of light as it crosses the boundary between two media
   b) a line drawn at 90° to a surface or boundary
   c) the material through which the light is travelling, e.g. glass, water, etc
   d) the splitting of white light into its component colours by refraction
   e) the band of colours produced by dispersion
   f) the chemical contained in an object which gives it its colour
   g) a piece of glass or plastic which only allows a certain colour of light to pass through it

Section C
1 a)

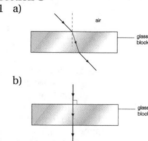

   b)

   c) travelling more slowly
2 a) spectrum
   b) rainbow
   c) only the red light

SOUNDS

Section A
1 a   2 d
3 b   4 c
5 d

Section B
1 vibrating, vibrate, high, vibrate, low, hertz, 5 Hz, amplitudes, amplitudes, quiet, solids, liquids, vacuum, faster, lightning, hear
2 a) D   b) B
   c) A   d) C

Section C

1. a) light waves travel much faster than sound waves
   b) it is reflected
2. a) the bell ringing
   b) the bell makes air particles vibrate, which in turn make John's eardrum vibrate
   c) No sound
   d) When there are no air particles in the jar there is no medium to carry the sound so John hears no ringing
   e) He can see the bell ringing even when all the air particles have been removed

ECHOES & HEARING

Section A

1	a	2	d
3	a	4	a
5	d		

Section B

1. a) echoes – reflections of sound waves from surfaces
   b) sonar – use of sound waves to measure the depth of the sea
   c) ultrasound – sound whose frequency is too high to be heard
   d) hearing range – spread of frequencies that can be heard
   e) reflected – bounced off
   f) decibel scale – scale used to measure the loudness of sounds
   g) loudness – the intensity of a sound
   h) ear defenders – equipment worn by people operating noisy machinery to prevent damage to hearing
2. a) 0 dB
   b) 50–60 dB
   c) 80–100 dB
   d) 20–30 dB
   e) 120–130 dB
   f) 10–20 dB

Section C

1. a) the spread of frequencies that can be heard
   b) 19 Hz
   c) 20 100 Hz
   d) Emma
   e) ultrasound
   f) bats, dogs, dolphins
2. a) to find the depth of the ocean below the ship
   b) a sound wave which has been reflected

ENERGY

Section A

1	d	2	c
3	b	4	c
5	a		

Section B

1. **Gravitational potential energy** The energy an object has when it is high.
   Sound energy Vibrating objects are sources of this energy.
   Electrical energy This energy is available every time a current flows.
   Chemical energy Food is an example of this.
   Light energy Most of your energy on earth begins as this.

Stored energy Forms of energy that are waiting to be used.
Nuclear energy The energy produced by reactions in the centre of an atom.
Kinetic energy The energy an object has because it is moving.
Elastic potential energy Winding up a spring will give it this type of energy.
Energy transfer When one type of energy changes into another type of energy.

2. a) Burning a candle changes chemical energy into heat and light energy.
   b) A loud speaker changes electrical energy into sound.
   c) A battery stores chemical energy.
   d) Water which is flowing has kinetic energy.
   e) Gravitational potential energy, elastic potential energy and chemical energy are all forms of stored energy.

Section C

1. a) chemical, kinetic, heat (sound)
   b) electrical, kinetic, sound
   c) electrical, heat, light
2. a) i) microphone
      ii) catapult or bow (and arrow)
      iii) cell or battery
   b) the food they eat
   c) the Sun
3. a) heat or thermal energy changes into gravitational potential energy
   b) gravitational potential energy changes into kinetic energy

USING ENERGY RESOURCES

Section A

1	a	2	b
3	b	4	d
5	d		

Section B

1. gas, fossil, sources, plants, animals, mud, pressure, temperature, fossil, non-renewable, replaced, acid rain, greenhouse effect
2. a) **fossil fuels** fuels composed of the fossilised remains of dead plants and animals
   b) **power station** place where fuels are converted into electrical energy
   c) **acid rain** unwanted pollutant created when some fossil fuels are burnt.
   d) **greenhouse effect** the gradual warming of the Earth's atmosphere caused by the release of carbon dioxide when fuels are burned
   e) **pollution** material released into the atmosphere which harms the environment
   f) **renewable** can be replaced
   g) **non-renewable** cannot be replaced

Section C

1. a) chemical energy
   b) by burning
   c) to heat water and change it into steam
   d) heat/thermal energy into kinetic energy
   e) kinetic energy into electrical energy
2. a) coal and oil
   b) once they have been used up they cannot be replaced
   c) greenhouse effect, acid rain, etc
   d) drive smaller cars, use public transport more often, insulate homes, develop more efficient cars, etc

ALTERNATIVE SOURCES OF ENERGY

Section A

1	c	2	b
3	c	4	d
5	a		

Section B

1. **Geothermal**
   + No pollution or environmental problems
   – Very few suitable sites
   Tidal
   + Reliable, two tides per day
   – Obstacle to water transport
   Wind
   + Low level technology
   – Possible visual and noise pollution
   Hydroelectric
   + Energy can be stored until required
   – High cost to environment i.e. flooding
   Wave
   + Useful for isolated islands
   – Poor energy capture
2. chemical, wood, Sun, renewable source, energy

Section C

1. a) coal, oil or gas
   b) wood/biomass
   c) wind and solar
   d) geothermal and tidal
   e)

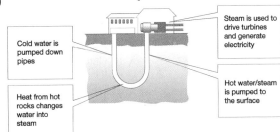

Cold water is pumped down pipes

Heat from hot rocks changes water into steam

Steam is used to drive turbines and generate electricity

Hot water/steam is pumped to the surface

f)

Gravitational potential energy of water	Kinetic energy of water	Kinetic energy of turbine	Electrical energy flows from the generator into the National Grid

g) it is in a high position and therefore has stored gravitational potential energy

HEAT TRANSFER

Section A

1	c	2	a
3	a	4	d
5	c		

Section B

1. a) true   b) false
   c) false   d) true

e)	true	f)	false
g)	true	h)	true
i)	true	j)	false
k)	false	l)	false

Section C

1. a) by radiation
   b) it is reflected
   c) it is absorbed
   d) the marble attached to the dark metal sheet will fall first
   e) the two sheets should be equidistant from the heater
2. loft insulation (fibre glass)
   cavity walls or cavity wall insulation
   install double glazing (accept fit thick curtains)
   fit carpets and even better also fit underlay
   fit draft excluders

CIRCUIT COMPONENTS

Section A

1	b	2	c
3	a	4	d
5	b		

Section B

1. charge, charges, cell, battery, wires, circuit, complete circuit, incomplete circuit, circuit diagrams, symbols.
2.

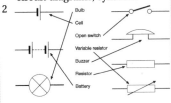

Bulb
Cell
Open switch
Variable resistor
Buzzer
Resistor
Battery

Section C

1. a) they should put their test material between the two crocodile clips. If the bulb glows the material is a conductor, if the bulb does not glow the material is an insulator
   b) Steel .... conductor, Paper... insulator, Bronze .... conductor, Graphite .... conductor, Mercury .... conductor.
   c) variable resistor
   d) ammeter
   e) it decreases
   f) bulb
   g) becomes dimmer
   h) dimmer switch in a cinema or theatre

CIRCUITS: CURRENT AND VOLTAGE

Section A
1 d   2 d
3 c   4 b
5 b

Section B
1 a) C or E
   b) E
   c) C and E
   d) C
2 a) ammeter
   b) amps or amperes

Section C
1 a) 1 and 2
   b) 1, 2 and 3
   c) C
2 0.1 A
3 a) 0.2 A
   b) electrical energy is changed into heat and light energy
   c) electrical energy is changed into heat energy

MAGNETS AND ELECTROMAGNETS

Section A
1 c   2 a
3 b   4 b
5 c

Section B
1
2

Section C
1 a)

b) more current and add more coils
c) strength of an electromagnet can be changed (turned on and off)
2 When the bell push is pressed the circuit is made complete and the electromagnet is turned on (1), the soft iron armature is pulled towards the electromagnet and the hammer hits the gong (1), a gap is created at the contact screw and the electromagnet is turned off (1), the armature springs back to its original position and the whole process starts again (1).

THE SOLAR SYSTEM 1

Section A
1 a   2 a
3 d   4 c
5 b

Section B

P	L	A	N	E	T	S
E	A	S	T		I	T
S		T		Y	L	A
U		E	M	E	T	R
M		R	O	A	S	S
M			O	O	R	
E	W	I	N	T	E	R
R		D	A	Y		
		S	W	E	S	T

a) STARS
b) MOON
c) PLANETS
d) ASTEROIDS
e) SUMMER and WINTER
f) WEST
g) EAST
h) TILTS
i) DAY
j) YEAR

Section C
1 a) Jupiter
   b) Mercury and Venus
   c) 84 years
   d) Mars
   e) Venus
   f) Jupiter
   g) the greater the distance from the Sun the longer the time to orbit the Sun
   h) Pluto
   i) It is the furthest planet from the Sun
   j) 4
   k) Neptune

THE SOLAR SYSTEM 2

Section A
1 c   2 c
3 a   4 c
5 a

Section B

a) etcmo	comet	A rock-like piece of ice that orbits the Sun
b) tanple	planet	A body which orbits a star or sun
c) arst	star	A luminous object in the sky
d) dasitero	asteroid	A lump of rock orbiting the Sun
e) nsu	sun	star at the centre of our solar system
f) onmo	moon	A natural satellite
g) asolr seeclip	solar eclipse	Sunlight blocked off by the Moon
h) lnura seplice	lunar eclipse	Sunlight blocked off from the Moon by the Earth
i) ravaait-tinglo of-serc	gravitational forces	Forces of attraction between astronomical bodies such as stars and planets and planets and satellites
j) laurn mthon	lunar month	The time it takes for the Moon to orbit the Earth

Section C
1 a) identical to diag on P123 of the guide
   b) Because all light from the Sun has been blocked off here.
   c) This diagram is identical to that for part a) but the positions of the Earth and the Moon have been interchanged. So the order from the left is Sun, Earth, Moon, No rays of light should be included on the relative positions are asked for.
2 a) gravitational forces
   b) When the comet is closest to the Sun
   c) when the comet is closest to the Sun
   d) vaporised ice.

ACKNOWLEDGEMENTS

The author and publisher are grateful to the copyright holders for permission to use quoted materials and photographs.

Letts Educational
4 Grosvenor Place
London SW1X 7DL
School enquiries: 01539 564910
Parent & student enquiries: 01539 564913
E-mail: mail@lettsed.co.uk
Website: www.letts-educational.com

First published 2007

© Brian Arnold, Hannah Kingston and Emma Poole 2007

Design and illustration ©2007 Letts Educational Ltd, a division of Huveaux Plc.

British Library Cataloguing in Publication Data. A CIP record of this book is available from the British Library.

ISBN 9781843157663

Book concept and development: Helen Jacobs, Letts and Lonsdale Publishing Director

Letts editorial team: Marion Davies and Alan Worth

Cover design: Angela English

Inside concept design: Starfish Design

Text design, layout and editorial: Servis Filmsetting

Letts and Lonsdale make every effort to ensure that all paper used in our books is made from wood pulp obtained from sustainable and well-managed forests.

C   These are SATs-style questions. Answer all parts of the questions.

1 The teacher reacted 4 metals with water and then with hydrochloric acid. He recorded his observations in the table below.

Metal	Observations when metal is reacted with water	Observations when metal is reacted with hydrochloric acid
silver	no reaction	no reaction
sodium	metal reacts vigorously producing bubbles of gas	too dangerous to carry out
magnesium	no reaction with cold water but steady reaction with steam	magnesium reacts quickly with acid, bubbles of gas are made as magnesium slowly dissolves
zinc	no reaction	steady reaction, bubbles of gas observed

a) Place the metals in order of reactivity.   (1 mark)

Most reactive ....

....

....

Least reactive ....

b) What is the name of the gas made when magnesium reacts with hydrochloric
acid? .... (1 mark)

c) What is the name of the salt formed when magnesium reacts with hydrochloric
acid? .... (1 mark)

d) Name a metal NOT mentioned in the table which reacts in a similar way to:

   i) silver .... (1 mark)

   ii) sodium .... (1 mark)

2 The equation below shows the reaction between calcium and hydrochloric acid.

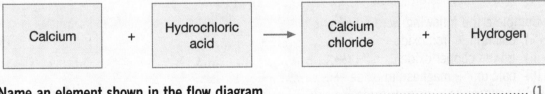

a) Name an element shown in the flow diagram. .... (1 mark)

b) Name a metal that reacts more vigorously than calcium. .... (1 mark)

c) Name a metal that reacts less vigorously than calcium. .... (1 mark)

Score   /8

How well did you do?   ✗ 1–7 Try again   8–18 Getting there   19–27 Good work   28–33 Excellent! ✓

For more information on this topic, see pages 56 & 64–65 of your Success Guide.

65

Displacement reactions

A more reactive metal will displace a less reactive metal from a compound.

A Choose just one answer, a, b, c or d.

1 Place these metals in order of reactivity (most reactive first) magnesium, copper, zinc, sodium. **(1 mark)**
a) magnesium, sodium, zinc, copper
b) sodium, magnesium, zinc, copper
c) sodium, magnesium, copper, zinc
d) magnesium, sodium, copper, zinc

2 Magnesium is more reactive than copper. What is formed when magnesium reacts with copper oxide? **(1 mark)**
a) magnesium sulphate + copper
b) magnesium + copper
c) magnesium oxide + copper
d) magnesium sulphate

3 Iron is more reactive than copper. What is formed when iron reacts with copper oxide? **(1 mark)**
a) iron + copper   b) iron oxide + copper
c) no reaction   d) iron sulphate + copper

4 Which of these metals is used to mend railway tracks? **(1 mark)**
a) copper   b) iron
c) sodium   d) magnesium

5 During the 'Thermit reaction' what is made?
a) iron **(1 mark)**
b) magnesium
c) aluminium
d) iron oxide

Score /5

B Answer all parts of the question.

Most reactive Calcium   Magnesium   Zinc   Iron   Copper Least reactive

1 a) Using the information from the table above, which of these reactions take place? Answer yes or no.
i) calcium + iron oxide **(1 mark)**
ii) copper + iron oxide **(1 mark)**
iii) magnesium + iron oxide **(1 mark)**
iv) iron + calcium oxide **(1 mark)**
v) iron + magnesium oxide **(1 mark)**

b) Complete the following word equations.
i) calcium + iron oxide → .... + ... **(2 marks)**
ii) iron + copper oxide → .... + ... **(2 marks)**
iii) calcium + magnesium oxide → .... + ... **(2 marks)**
iv) magnesium + copper oxide → .... + ... **(2 marks)**
v) magnesium + iron oxide → .... + ... **(2 marks)**

c) Complete the following symbol equations.
i) $Zn + FeSO_4$ → .... + Fe **(1 mark)**
ii) $Mg +$ .... → $MgSO_4 + Cu$ **(1 mark)**
iii) $Zn + CuSO_4$ → $ZnSO_4 +$ .... **(1 mark)**
iv) $Mg + FeSO_4$ → .... + ... **(2 marks)**
v) $Fe + CuSO_4$ → .... + ... **(2 marks)**

Score /22

66

C This is a SATs-style question. Answer all parts of the question.

1 Britney has four different metals and four different metal sulphate solutions. Britney placed a couple of drops of each solution onto a spotting tile and then added a small piece of each metal. Britney recorded her results in the table below. A tick shows that a reaction had taken place, a cross shows that no reaction had taken place.

Metal/metal sulphate solution	Copper sulphate	Magnesium sulphate	Iron sulphate	Zinc sulphate
copper	✗	....	✗	....
magnesium	✓	✗	....	✓
iron	....	✗	✗	✗
zinc	✓	✗	✓	✗

a) Complete the table to show which reactions take place.   (4 marks)

b) Place the four metals in order of reactivity.   (1 mark)

   most reactive ...., ..., ..., ... least reactive

c) Imagine that a new metal has been discovered on another planet. It has the name shinium. Shinium displaces both copper from a solution of copper sulphate and zinc from a solution of zinc sulphate. Magnesium can displace shinium from the compound shinium oxide. Rewrite the order of reactivity to include the new metal shinium.   (1 mark)

   most reactive ...., ..., ..., ..., ... least reactive

d) The list below shows the names and symbols of five elements. The elements have been placed in order of reactivity.

   most reactive Potassium, Sodium, Magnesium, Zinc, Copper **least reactive**
   (K)   (Na)   (Mg)   (Zn)   (Cu)

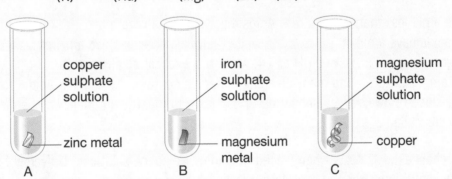

   A   B   C

   In test tube A, Britney noticed that the zinc metal became covered in a brown deposit.

   i)   What is the name of the brown deposit? .... (1 mark)

   ii) Write a word equation for the reaction that takes place in test tube B. .... (1 mark)

e) Write a balanced symbol equation for the reaction between magnesium (Mg) and iron sulphate ($FeSO_4$)... (1 mark)

   Score   /9

How well did you do?   ✗ 1–7 **Try again**   8–18 **Getting there**   19–28 **Good work**   29–36 **Excellent!** ✓

For more information on this topic, see pages 66–67 of your Success Guide.

67

Acids and alkalis

Indicators are used to show whether a solution is acidic, alkaline or neutral by changing colour.

A Choose just one answer, a, b, c or d.

1 What is the pH of a strong alkali?   (1 mark)
   a) 6   b) 7
   c) 14   d) 1

2 Which chemical is a strong acid?   (1 mark)
   a) sodium hydroxide
   b) sulphuric acid
   c) calcium hydroxide
   d) potassium hydroxide

3 If a soil is too acidic, what should a farmer add to it?   (1 mark)
   a) compost   b) lime
   c) water   d) battery acid

4 What is formed when an acid reacts with an alkali?   (1 mark)
   a) salt + hydrogen
   b) salt only
   c) salt + water
   d) sodium hydroxide

5 Which of these chemicals can be found in indigestion tablets?   (1 mark)
   a) hydrochloric acid
   b) calcium carbonate
   c) sodium hydroxide
   d) sulphuric acid

Score   /5

B Answer all parts of the question.

1 Complete the following passage.   (21 marks)

Acids have a pH less than .... Acids react with alkalis to form .... solutions. The strongest acids have a pH of ...., while the weakest acids have a pH of ....
The strongest .... have a pH of 14, while the weakest alkalis have a pH of .... Many foods contain .... and many cleaning materials contain .... Acidic foods have a .... taste. However, you should never use taste to identify an unknown chemical. Instead we use chemicals called ....

Indicators change .... when placed in acidic or alkaline solutions. Universal .... is a particularly useful indicator, not only does it show whether a solution is acidic or alkaline, it also shows how .... or how .... the solution is. The strongest .... turn Universal Indicator red. Weaker acids like rainwater, which has a pH of around 5, turn Universal Indicator .... .The weakest acids turn Universal Indicator ....
Weak .... turn Universal Indicator blue, while stronger alkalis turn Universal Indicator ....

.... are often more corrosive than acids of the same strength, so always ensure that you wear .... when using either of these two types of chemical.

Score   /21

C These are SATs-style questions. Answer all parts of the questions.

1 The table below shows the pH of five different shampoos.

Shampoo	pH
Shimmer and Shine	5.4
Silky	6.9
Shine-a-Lot	7.4
Healthy Hair	7.6
Super Shine	10.1

Use the table to answer the following questions.

a) Which shampoo is the strongest acid? .... (1 mark)

b) Which shampoo is the weakest alkali? .... (1 mark)

c) Tick ONE of the boxes below to show which description best describes the shampoo 'Silky'. (1 mark)

strongly acidic ☐

weakly acidic ☐

neutral ☐

weakly alkaline ☐

strongly alkaline ☐

The chart below shows the colour of Universal Indicator in different types of solution.

Description of solution	Strong acid	Weak acid	Neutral	Weak alkali	Strong alkali
Colour of Universal Indicator	red	orange	green	blue	purple

d) What colour will the shampoo 'Shimmer and Shine' turn Universal Indicator? (1 mark)

....

e) What colour will the shampoo 'Healthy Hair' turn Universal Indicator? (1 mark)

....

2 The table below shows the pH value of soil below which various plants do not thrive.

Plant	pH below which it does not thrive
potato	5.0
cabbage	6.2
carrot	6.5

a) Which of these three crops can continue to grow in the most acidic conditions? (1 mark)

....

b) What can be applied to the soil to increase the pH of the soil? (1 mark)

....

Score /7

How well did you do? ✗ 1–11 Try again   12–21 Getting there   22–27 Good work   28–33 Excellent! ✓

For more information on this topic, see pages 68–69 of your Success Guide.

69

Making salts

Metals can be reacted with acids to form a salt and hydrogen.

A Choose just one answer, a, b, c or d.

1 Which of these chemicals is a base? **(1 mark)**
a) lemon juice   b) hydrochloric acid
c) sulphuric acid   d) calcium carbonate

2 Name the products formed when zinc reacts
with hydrochloric acid.   **(1 mark)**
a) zinc sulphate + water
b) zinc chloride + water
c) zinc sulphate + hydrogen
d) zinc chloride + hydrogen

3 Name the products formed when zinc oxide
reacts with hydrochloric acid.   **(1 mark)**
a) zinc sulphate + hydrogen
b) zinc chloride + hydrogen
c) zinc chloride + water
d) zinc sulphate + water

4 Name the products formed when zinc
carbonate reacts with sulphuric acid.   **(1 mark)**
a) zinc sulphate + water + carbon dioxide
b) copper nitrate + water + carbon dioxide
c) zinc sulphate + hydrogen
d) zinc sulphate + water

5 Name the products formed when copper oxide
reacts with hydrochloric acid.   **(1 mark)**
a) copper sulphate
b) copper chloride + hydrogen
c) copper chloride + water
d) copper sulphate + water

Score   /5

B Answer all parts of all questions.

1 The instructions below show the steps needed to make the salt copper sulphate from copper
carbonate and sulphuric acid, but the order of the steps has been jumbled up. Write the
sentences in the correct order to explain how the salt can be made.   **(5 marks)**

a) It is heated until the first crystal appears.

b) Copper carbonate is added to the acid until it stops fizzing.

c) The solution is poured into an evaporating dish.

d) The solution is then left for a few days for the copper sulphate to crystallise.

e) The unreacted copper carbonate is then removed by filtering.

2 Complete the following word equations.

a) zinc + sulphuric acid → zinc sulphate + ...   **(1 mark)**

b) .... + hydrochloric acid → magnesium chloride + hydrogen   **(1 mark)**

c) copper carbonate + sulphuric acid → .... + water + carbon dioxide   **(1 mark)**

d) zinc carbonate + nitric acid → zinc nitrate + ... + ...   **(2 marks)**

e) zinc oxide + nitric acid → zinc nitrate + ...   **(1 mark)**

f) copper oxide + ... → copper sulphate + water   **(1 mark)**

Score   /12

70

C This is a SATs-style question. Answer all parts of the question.

1 The table below shows the names and formulae of six compounds.

Name of compound	Formula of compound
hydrochloric acid	HCl
sulphuric acid	H_2SO_4
copper oxide	CuO
copper carbonate	$CuCO_3$
copper sulphate	$CuSO_4$
copper chloride	$CuCl_2$

a) Complete the word equation below to show the reaction between copper carbonate and
   hydrochloric acid. (3 marks)

   copper carbonate + hydrochloric acid ➜ .... + ... + ...

b) Complete and balance the equations below to show the reactions between

   i) copper oxide and sulphuric acid (2 marks)

   $CuO + H_2SO_4$ ➜ .... + ...

   ii) copper carbonate and sulphuric acid (3 marks)

   $CuCO_3 + H_2SO_4$ ➜ .... + ... + ...

c) Sulphuric acid has the formula H_2SO_4.

   i) How many atoms of hydrogen are represented in this formula?.....................................(1 mark)

   ii) How many atoms of sulphur are represented in this formula? ....(1 mark)

   iii) How many atoms of oxygen are represented in this formula? ....(1 mark)

   iv) How many atoms overall are represented in this formula? ....(1 mark)

   Score   /12

How well did you do? ✗ 1–8 Try again 9–14 Getting there 15–21 Good work 22–29 Excellent! ✓

For more information on this topic, see pages 68–71 & 83 of your Success Guide.

Chemical tests

Some common chemicals can be tested for using simple tests.

A

Choose just one answer, a, b, c or d.

1 Which gas burns with a 'squeaky pop'? (1 mark)

a) hydrogen b) oxygen
c) helium d) carbon dioxide

2 Which gas forms a white suspension with limewater (makes the limewater milky)? (1 mark)

a) oxygen b) carbon dioxide
c) helium d) hydrogen

3 A chemical can cause death if swallowed, breathed in or absorbed through the skin. Which hazard symbol should it bear? (1 mark)

a) corrosive b) highly flammable
c) toxic d) irritant

4 A chemical can catch fire very easily. Which hazard symbol should it bear? (1 mark)

a) highly flammable
b) toxic
c) corrosive
d) irritant

5 A chemical can attack and destroy living tissue such as eyes and skin. Which hazard symbol should it bear? (1 mark)

a) highly flammable b) toxic
c) corrosive d) irritant

Score /5

B

Answer all parts of all questions.

1 Carbon dioxide (10 marks)

Limewater is used to test for the gas .... The gas is .... through the limewater. If the limewater turns .... the gas is carbon dioxide.

Hydrogen

The gas hydrogen is tested for using a .... splint. If hydrogen is present it will burn with a ....

Oxygen

The gas .... is needed for things to burn. Things burn more brightly in pure oxygen than they do in .... If a .... splint is placed in a test tube containing oxygen, the splint ....

2 Complete these word equations.

a) copper + ... → copper oxide (1 mark)

b) magnesium + hydrochloric acid → magnesium chloride + ... (1 mark)

c) copper carbonate + nitric acid → copper nitrate + water + ... (1 mark)

d) zinc + sulphuric acid → zinc sulphate + ... (1 mark)

e) zinc carbonate + sulphuric acid → zinc sulphate + water + ... (1 mark)

f) carbon + ... → carbon dioxide (1 mark)

Score /16

C These are SATs-style questions. Answer all parts of the questions.

1 Some chemicals are dangerous and should only be used with great care. Containers holding these chemicals are marked with a label which gives information about that chemical. **(4 marks)**

Below are four hazard symbols and four hazard descriptions. Draw a line to connect each symbol to the correct description.

Hazard symbols

Description of hazard

Corrosive

Attacks and destroys living tissues including eyes and skin.

Harmful

Similar to toxic, but less dangerous.

Highly flammable

Catches fire easily.

Toxic

Can cause death if swallowed, breathed in or absorbed through the skin.

2 When toast is burnt it changes colour. Two gases are produced when toast is burnt. One gas is water vapour. When the other gas is bubbled though limewater it turns the limewater cloudy.

a) Name the gas, found in the air, which is needed for the toast to burn. **(1 mark)**

....

b) Name the gas produced when toast is burnt, which turns limewater cloudy. **(1 mark)**

....

Score /6

How well did you do? ✗ 1–7 **Try again** 8–12 **Getting there** 13–19 **Good work** 20–27 **Excellent!** ✓

For more information on this topic, see pages 62 & 70–73 of your Success Guide.

73

Mixtures

A mixture contains two or more elements or compounds that are not joined together. Generally, mixtures are quite easy to separate.

A Choose just one answer, a, b, c or d.

1 Which element is the main gas in air? **(1 mark)**
a) oxygen b) nitrogen
c) carbon dioxide d) carbon monoxide

2 Which element makes up 20 per cent of air? **(1 mark)**
a) oxygen b) nitrogen
c) carbon dioxide d) helium

3 What do most rocks consist of? **(1 mark)**
a) a mixture of different minerals
b) different minerals in fixed amounts
c) calcium carbonate
d) gold

4 Why is a mixture different from a compound?
a) mixtures cannot be separated **(1 mark)**
b) particles are joined in a mixture
c) particles are not joined in a mixture
d) mixtures are dangerous to pets

5 Which minerals are found in granite? **(1 mark)**
a) limestone and quartz
b) feldspar, quartz and mica
c) mica and fluorite
d) rock salt and basalt

Score /5

B Answer all parts of all questions.

1 Consider these substances **(9 marks)**

butter   silicon dioxide   oxygen   sea water   neon
water   air   granite   sodium chloride

Complete the table below to show whether each of these substances is a mixture, a pure compound or a pure element.

Mixtures	Pure compounds	Pure elements

2 Complete the passage below. **(13 marks)**

Air is a .... of gases. About 78% of the air around you is .... Nitrogen is an element with the symbol N. Roughly 20% of air is .... Oxygen is also an .... and has the symbol O. Both nitrogen and oxygen occur as molecules; nitrogen occurs as N_2 and oxygen occurs as .... Air also contains small amounts of other gases including .... dioxide, water .... and the noble gases .... and ....

Most rocks are mixtures of different .... A mineral is a .... because it has a fixed composition. The igneous rock granite contains a mixture of different minerals including feldspar, ... and mica. The exact proportion of these .... varies from one piece of granite to another and is not fixed.

Score /22

C

These are SATs-style questions. Answer all parts of the questions.

1 The table below shows the melting points and boiling points of four gases.

Gas	Melting point °C	Boiling point °C
oxygen	−218	−183
nitrogen	−210	−196
argon	−189	−186
neon	−248	−246

a) Which of these gases has the lowest boiling point? .... (1 mark)

b) Which of these gases has the highest melting point? .... (1 mark)

c) Oxygen is an element that can exist as a solid, a liquid or a gas. When oxygen is cooled from room temperature to −**247**°C it changes state from
.... to ....   (2 marks)

2 The diagrams below show the particle arrangements in six different substances.

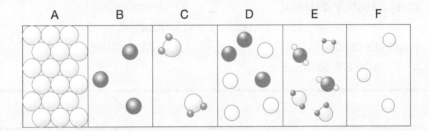

Give the letter of the diagram that best represents the arrangement of particles in:

a) a mixture of two elements.. (1 mark)

b) a mixture of two compounds. .... (1 mark)

c) In an experiment a gas jar containing substance B and a second gas jar containing substance F were placed together. The substances were left for 10 minutes and DID NOT react.   (1 mark)

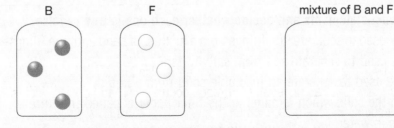

Complete the box on the right to show how the particles are arranged in a mixture of B and F.

Score /7

How well did you do?   ✗ 1–9 Try again   10–19 Getting there   20–27 Good work   28–34 Excellent! ✓

For more information on this topic, see pages 51, 56 & 74–75 of your Success Guide.

75

Separation techniques

In a mixture the constituent parts are not joined together. Mixtures can be separated quite easily.

A Choose just one answer, a, b, c or d.

1 How could a mixture of alcohol and water be separated? **(1 mark)**
a) chromatography   b) fractional
c) filtration   distillation
d) recrystallisation

2 How could the different coloured dyes in green food colouring be separated? **(1 mark)**
a) chromatography   b) distillation
c) filtration   d) recrystallisation

3 During chromatography, why does each of the coloured dyes travel a slightly different distance? **(1 mark)**
a) different solvents are used
b) they have slightly different solubilities

c) different paper is used
d) red dyes always travel faster

4 What is the name of the piece of equipment in which water vapour is turned back into liquid water? **(1 mark)**
a) liquidiser   b) spectrometer
c) thermometer   d) condenser

5 How can a solvent be separated from a solution? **(1 mark)**
a) distillation
b) chromatography
c) filtration
d) crystallisation

Score   /5

B Answer all parts of all questions.

1 There are many different methods that can be used to separate mixtures. Draw a line to link each mixture to the correct technique for separating it. **(5 marks)**

Mixtures	Technique
a salt like sodium chloride from salty water	magnet
the colours in fountain pen ink	fractional distillation
iron from iron filings and sand	filtering
water from alcohol and water	evaporation
mud from muddy water	chromatography

2 Consider the following statements and decide whether each one is true or false.
a) A magnet can be used to separate iron filings from a mixture of sand and iron filings. ....(1 mark)
b) Filtering can be used to separate salt from salty water. .... (1 mark)
c) Filtration can be used to separate an insoluble solid from a liquid. .... (1 mark)
d) During filtration the solid which remains in the filter paper is called the filtrate.............. (1 mark)
e) Salt is insoluble in water. .... (1 mark)
f) Sand can be separated from a mixture of salt and sand by dissolving the salt in water and then filtering the mixture. .... (1 mark)
g) Chromatography can be used to separate mixtures of the different coloured dyes in orange food colouring... (1 mark)

Score   /12

C This is a SATs-style question. Answer all parts of the question.

1 Karl has two black felt tip pens. He labels them **A** and **B**.

Karl wants to identify the different coloured inks found in each of his pens and carries out the experiment shown below.

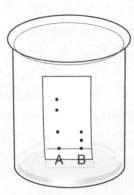

a) What is the name given to this method of separating mixtures of different coloured
dyes?.. (1 mark)

Karl then repeated the experiment using his other coloured felt tip pens.

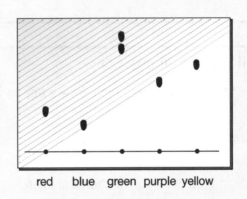

b) Use Karl's results to identify a felt tip pen whose ink is made of two coloured dyes.   (1 mark)

....

c) i) Identify the three coloured dyes in black felt tip pen A. .... (1 mark)

   ii) Identify the two coloured dyes in black felt tip pen B. .... (1 mark)

Score   /4

How well did you do?   ✗ 1–4 **Try again**   5–8 **Getting there**   9–15 **Good work**   16–21 **Excellent!** ✓

For more information on this topic, see pages 76–77 of your Success Guide.

77

Compounds

If atoms of two or more elements are joined together they form a compound. Compounds have a fixed composition.

A — Choose just one answer, a, b, c or d.

1 Which of these statements is true of sulphur? **(1 mark)**
a) it's magnetic b) it's a grey solid
c) it's a yellow solid d) it's a compound

2 Which of these statements is true of iron?
a) it's a yellow solid b) it's a magnetic metal **(1 mark)**
c) it's a compound
d) it's non magnetic

3 Which of these statements is true of iron sulphate? **(1 mark)**
a) it's an element b) it's magnetic
c) it's yellow d) it's a compound

4 How could a mixture of iron and sulphur be separated? **(1 mark)**
a) use a magnet
b) distillation
c) it cannot be separated
d) dissolving and recrystallisation

5 How could iron sulphide be separated to give iron and sulphur? **(1 mark)**
a) it cannot be easily separated
b) use a magnet
c) distillation
d) dissolving and recrystallisation

Score /5

B — Answer all parts of all questions.

1 Rearrange the following anagrams then draw a line to join the word you have found to its correct definition. **(5 marks)**

Anagrams	Definitions
cduopomn	a chemical change
yeproprt	a small piece of a substance which has all the properties of the substance
eeculomc	a substance which is made of atoms of two or more elements that have been chemically joined together
mentag	a substance which does, or can, attract other materials
icatreno	a quality which is always present in a substance, however much of it is present

2 Complete the passage below. **(10 marks)**

Elements are made of only one type of .... If atoms of the same elements are joined together they form .... of the element. The oxygen and nitrogen in the air around us are in the form of molecules.

B (Continued)

If the atoms of two (or more) different elements are chemically joined together they form molecules of a .... New substances are formed by chemical .... These new substances are called the .... The products of a chemical reaction can have very different properties from the .... at the start of the reaction. When iron and sulphur are heated together they can form a new substance called .... Iron is a magnetic .... Sulphur is a .... solid. But, ... has very different properties from both iron and sulphur – it is a non-magnetic black solid.

Score   /15

C

These are SATs-style questions. Answer all parts of the questions.

1 Nikesh placed a flask containing 75 cm^3 of acid on a balance. He added 5 g of magnesium carbonate.

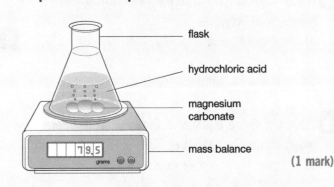

How could Nikesh tell that a chemical reaction was taking place?

(1 mark)

....

....

2 Nikesh's experiment can be represented by this word equation:

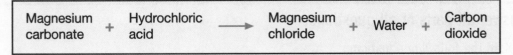

| Magnesium carbonate | + | Hydrochloric acid | → | Magnesium chloride | + | Water | + | Carbon dioxide |

a) **During the reaction the mass of the flask and the chemicals goes down. A little of the water evaporates to form water vapour.**

(2 marks)

i) What else can have caused the decrease in mass? ....

ii) Name one of the reactants in Nikesh's experiment. ....

b) **The diagram below shows how the particles are arranged in four substances.**

(1 mark)

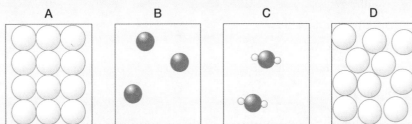

A   B   C   D

Write the letter of the diagram which best represents the carbon dioxide gas produced in Nikesh's experiment. ....

Score   /4

How well did you do? ✗ 1–4 Try again   5–9 Getting there   10–16 Good work   17–24 Excellent! ✓

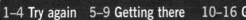
For more information on this topic, see pages 78–79 of your Success Guide.

Naming compounds

When atoms of two or more elements join together they form a compound. Compounds are generally difficult to separate.

A   Choose just one answer, a, b, c or d.

1 Name the compound formed when iron is burnt in air. **(1 mark)**
a) rust
b) iron oxide
c) iron
d) steel

2 Name the compound formed when magnesium reacts with bromine. **(1 mark)**
a) magnesium iodide
b) magnesium chloride
c) magnesium oxide
d) magnesium bromide

3 Which of these equations shows what happens when copper is heated in air? **(1 mark)**
a) copper + oxygen → copper oxide
b) copper + air → copper dioxide
c) copper + oxygen → copper
d) copper oxide + oxygen → copper

4 Which of these equations shows what happens when magnesium is burnt in air? **(1 mark)**
a) magnesium + oxygen → magnesium oxide
b) magnesium + nitrogen → magnesium oxide
c) magnesium + oxygen → magnesium nitride
d) magnesium oxide → magnesium + oxygen

5 Which of these equations shows what happens when sodium reacts with chlorine? **(1 mark)**
a) sodium + chloride → sodium chlorine
b) sodium + chlorine → sodium chlorine
c) sodium + chlorine → sodium oxide
d) sodium + chlorine → sodium chloride

Score   /5

B   Answer all parts of all questions.

1 Complete the following equations.
a) sodium + ... → sodium oxide   (1 mark)
b) iron + ... → iron sulphide   (1 mark)
c) copper + oxygen → ....   (1 mark)
d) sodium + fluorine → ....   (1 mark)
e) sodium + ... → sodium chloride   (1 mark)
f) magnesium + ... → magnesium oxide   (1 mark)
g) potassium + iodine → ....   (1 mark)
h) .... + oxygen → zinc oxide   (1 mark)
i) .... + hydrogen → water   (1 mark)
j) carbon + ... → carbon dioxide   (1 mark)

2 Name these compounds.
a) KOH..(1 mark)
b) $MgCO_3$..(1 mark)
c) $FeSO_4$ ....(1 mark)
d) CaO..(1 mark)
e) KCl ....(1 mark)

Score   /15

C These are SATs-style questions. Answer all parts of the questions.

1 Sedimentary rocks can form when seawater evaporates leaving behind minerals called evaporites. The table below shows the name and formula of some common evaporite minerals.

Mineral	Formula
halite	NaCl
anhydrite	$CaSO_4$
sylvine	KCl

a) Give the chemical name of the minerals   (2 marks)

   i) halite

   ....

   ii) sylvine

   ....

b) Another common mineral found in sedimentary rocks is barytes, $BaSO_4$.

   i) How many different elements are present in the mineral barytes?   (1 mark)

   ....

   ii) How many atoms of oxygen are represented by the formula for barytes?   (1 mark)

   ....

   iii) How many atoms altogether are represented by the formula for barytes?   (1 mark)

   ....

2 Tom has been given a sample of a green powder. The green powder can be represented by the formula $CuCO_3$.   (2 marks)

Tick the boxes below to show what the formula tells Tom about the powder. Tick two boxes.

a) It is an element.   ☐

b) It is a compound.   ☐

c) It is a carbonate.   ☐

d) It is an oxide.   ☐

Score   /7

How well did you do?   ✗ 1–7 Try again   8–12 Getting there   13–19 Good work   20–27 Excellent! ✓

For more information on this topic, see pages 62, 64 & 80–81 of your Success Guide.

Balancing equations

In science, elements and compounds can be represented by simple symbols.

A Choose just one answer, a, b, c or d.

1 Look at the formula for calcium carbonate, $CaCO_3$. How many carbon atoms are present?
a) 1   b) 2   c) 3   d) 4 **(1 mark)**

2 Look at the formula for carbon dioxide, CO_2. How many oxygen atoms are present? **(1 mark)**
a) 2   b) 1   c) 3   d) 4

3 Which of these statements is true? **(1 mark)**
a) In chemical reactions, the reactants have a greater mass than the products.
b) In chemical reactions, the overall mass before and after is the same.
c) In chemical reactions, the products have a greater mass than the reactants.
d) If a gas is made in a reaction it will have no mass.

4 The equation $Na + Cl_2 \rightarrow NaCl$ is not balanced. Which of these equations shows how the equation should be balanced correctly?
(1 mark)
a) $2Na + Cl_2 \rightarrow NaCl$
b) $2Na + Cl_2 \rightarrow 2NaCl$
c) $Na + Cl_2 \rightarrow NaCl_2$
d) $Na + Cl_2 \rightarrow 2NaCl$

5 The equation $H_2 + Cl_2 \rightarrow HCl$ is not balanced. Which of these equations shows how the equation should be balanced correctly? **(1 mark)**
a) $H_2 + Cl_2 \rightarrow 2HCl$ b) $2H_2 + Cl_2 \rightarrow 2HCl$
c) $H_2 + 2Cl_2 \rightarrow 2HCl$
d) $2H_2 + 2Cl_2 \rightarrow 2HCl$

Score /5

B Answer all parts of all questions.

1 a) Magnesium carbonate has the formula $MgCO_3$.
i) How many magnesium atoms are represented in this formula? ....(1 mark)
ii) How many carbon atoms are represented in this formula? ....(1 mark)
iii) How many oxygen atoms are represented in this formula? ....(1 mark)

b) Zinc sulphate has the formula $ZnSO_4$.
i) How many zinc atoms are represented in this formula? ....(1 mark)
ii) How many sulphur atoms are represented in this formula? ....(1 mark)
iii) How many oxygen atoms are represented in this formula? ....(1 mark)

c) Hexane has the formula C_6H_{14}.
i) How many carbon atoms are represented in this formula? ....(1 mark)
ii) How many hydrogen atoms are represented in this formula? ....(1 mark)

2 Complete the following equations.
a) ....H_2 + ...I_2 → .... HI   (1 mark)
b) ....H_2 + ...Cl_2 → .... HCl   (1 mark)
c) ....H_2 + ...O_2 → .... H_2O (1 mark)
d) ....Mg + ...HCl → ....$MgCl_2$ + ...H_2 (1 mark)
e) ....Zn + ...H_2SO_4 → ....$ZnSO_4$ + ...H_2 (1 mark)

Score /13

Chemistry   BALANCING EQUATIONS

C

These are SATs-style questions. Answer all parts of the questions.

1 The salt sodium sulphate can be made by reacting sodium hydroxide with sulphuric acid.

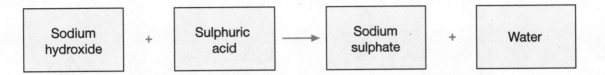

Sodium hydroxide + Sulphuric acid → Sodium sulphate + Water

a) Why is sodium sulphate NOT made by reacting sulphuric acid directly with the metal sodium? (1 mark)

....

b) The formula for sodium sulphate is Na_2SO_4.

   i) How many atoms of sodium are represented by this formula? (1 mark)

   ....

   ii) How many atoms of sulphur are represented by this formula? (1 mark)

   ....

   iii) How many atoms of oxygen are represented by this formula? (1 mark)

   ....

   iv) How many atoms overall are represented by this formula? (1 mark)

   ....

c) The reaction between sodium hydroxide and sulphuric acid can be represented using a symbol equation. Balance the equation below to show this reaction. (2 marks)

   ....NaOH + ...H_2SO_4 → ....Na_2SO_4 + ...H_2O

2 Libby heats a small piece of copper metal in a Bunsen burner flame. After heating, Libby notices that the metal has changed colour and is now black.

a) Libby has made a new compound. What is the name of the new compound? (1 mark)

....

b) This reaction can be represented by a symbol equation. Balance the equation below to show Libby's reaction. (2 marks)

   ....Cu + O_2 → ....CuO

Score   /10

How well did you do?   ✗ 1–7 Try again   8–14 Getting there   15–21 Good work   22–28 Excellent! ✓

For more information on this topic, see pages 64 & 82–83 of your Success Guide.

Speed

The speed of an object tells us how fast it is moving.

A Choose just one answer, a, b, c or d.

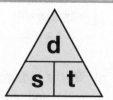

Use this formula triangle to help you answer some of the questions on this section of work.

1 What is the speed of a sprinter who runs 160 m in 20 s? *(1 mark)*
a) 0.8 m/s   b) 320 m/s
c) 32 m/s   d) 8 m/s

2 What is the speed of a train that travels 240 km in 3 hours? *(1 mark)*
a) 80 km/h   b) 720 km/h
c) 80 m/s   d) 720 m/s

3 How long will it take a man running at 10 m/s to travel 500 m? *(1 mark)*
a) 5 s   b) 50 s
c) 5000 s   d) 0.5 h

4 How long will it take a car travelling at 120 km/h to complete a journey of 60 km?
a) 2 h   b) 2 mins   *(1 mark)*
c) 0.5 h   d) 1 h

5 How far will a bus travel in 5 hours if its speed is 60 km/h?   *(1 mark)*
a) 12 km
b) 24 km
c) 300 km
d) 120 km

Score   /5

B Answer all parts of all questions. Show all your working for numerical questions.

1 Calculate the speed of a car that travels:
a) 500 m in 20 s .... (1 mark)
b) 6000 m in 1 min .... (1 mark)
c) 800 km in 4 hours. .... (1 mark)

2 Calculate the distance travelled by a pupil who cycles at:
a) 25 m/s for 40 s .... (1 mark)
b) 18 m/s for 50 s .... (1 mark)
c) 30 m/s for 2 min. .... (1 mark)

3 Calculate the time it takes a jogger to:
a) run 200 m whilst jogging at a speed of 4 m/s .... (1 mark)
b) run 1 km whilst jogging at 5 m/s .... (1 mark)
c) run 10 km whilst jogging at 4 km/h. .... (1 mark)

4 Which is travelling faster, a cyclist who travels 400 m in 20 s or a skier who travels 1500 m in 1 min? .... (1 mark)

5 Who will travel further, a woman who runs at 5 m/s for 1 hour or an aircraft that travels at 180 m/s for 2 min? .... (1 mark)

6 Whose journey takes the longer, a driver travelling 400 km at an average speed of 80 km/h or a pilot travelling 8000 km at an average speed of 1500 km/h?   *(1 mark)*

....

Score   /12

1 Katy and Richard are carrying out an experiment to discover the average speed of a trolley as it travels down their runway.

a) What two pieces of apparatus not shown in the above diagram will the two pupils need to carry out their investigation? (2 marks)

....

....

b) Suggest two variables Katy and Richard need to control in order to make sure that they carry out a fair test. (2 marks)

....

....

c) What effect do you think increasing the angle of the runway will have on the average speed of the trolley? (1 mark)

....

....

d) A skier takes 4 s to travel down a slope 50 m long. Calculate the average speed of the skier on the slope. (3 marks)

....

....

e) Suggest one way in which the skier could increase his average speed down the slope. (1 mark)

....

....

Score   /9

Graphs of motion

It is often useful to show the motion of an object in the form of a graph. There are two types of graph you should be familiar with: distance–time graphs and speed–time graphs.

A Choose just one answer, a, b, c or d.

1 A sloping straight line on a distance–time graph tells us that the object is: **(1 mark)**
a) accelerating
b) going up hill
c) decelerating
d) moving at a constant speed

2 What does the gradient of a line on a distance–time graph tell us about an object? **(1 mark)**
a) its direction
b) its acceleration
c) its speed
d) the steepness of the hill it is climbing

3 A line which is sloping upwards on a speed–time graph tells us that the object is: **(1 mark)**
a) travelling at a constant speed
b) accelerating
c) going uphill
d) stationary

4 A steep line on a distance–time graph tells us that the object is: **(1 mark)**
a) moving at a high speed
b) travelling up a steep hill
c) travelling at a constant speed
d) accelerating quickly

5 A steep line sloping upwards on a speed–time graph tells us that the object is: **(1 mark)**
a) moving with a high acceleration
b) travelling up a steep hill
c) travelling at a high constant speed
d) decelerating

Score   /5

B Answer all parts of all questions. Show all your working for numerical questions.

1 The distance–time graph below shows the journey of a walker.

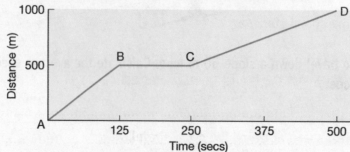

a) During which part of the journey was the walker stationary? .... **(1 mark)**

b) For how long was the walker stationary? .... **(1 mark)**

c) During which part of the journey was the walker moving fastest? .... **(1 mark)**

d) Calculate the fastest speed of the walker. .... **(1 mark)**

e) What is the total distance travelled by the walker? .... **(1 mark)**

f) Calculate the average speed of the walker for the whole journey. .... **(1 mark)**

Score   /6

1 The speed–time graph for a
car journey is shown opposite.

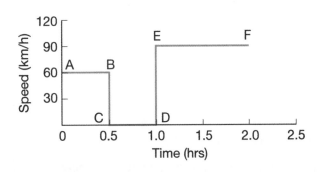

a) During which part of the journey was the car stationary? .... (1 mark)

b) For how long was the car stationary? .... (1 mark)

c) During which part of the journey was the car moving fastest? .... (1 mark)

d) What was the fastest speed of the car? .... (1 mark)

e) Calculate the total distance travelled by the car. .... (1 mark)

f) Calculate the average speed of the car for the whole journey. .... (1 mark)

2 Each minute Jill measured the distance travelled by a cyclist during his 8 minute journey.
She recorded her results in the table shown below.

Time in minutes	0	1	2	3	4	5	6	7	8
Distance travelled in metres	0	200	400	600	600	600	1000	1400	1800

a) Draw a distance–time graph for the
journey of the cyclist.

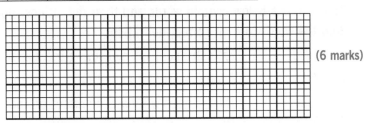

(6 marks)

b) For how long was the cyclist stationary?
(1 mark)

....

c) Between which readings was the cyclist travelling fastest?
(1 mark)

....

d) Calculate the greatest speed at which the cyclist travelled.
(3 marks)

....

e) Calculate the average speed for the cyclist's journey.
(3 marks)

....

Score   /20

GRAPHS OF MOTION   Physics

How well did you do?   1–11 Try again   12–19 Getting there   20–26 Good work   27–31 Excellent!

For more help on this topic see KS3 Science Success Guide pages 88–89

87

Forces

Most forces are pushes or pulls. They can affect the motion and shape of an object.

A — Choose just one answer, a, b, c or d.

1 Which of the following will happen if balanced forces are applied to an object? **(1 mark)**
a) it will accelerate
b) it will decelerate
c) it may travel at a constant speed
d) it will change direction

2 Which of the following is not an example of balanced forces? **(1 mark)**
a) a cork floating on water
b) a box on a table
c) a car accelerating
d) a weight hanging from a spring

3 The force exerted on an object by gravity is called the object's: **(1 mark)**
a) weight   b) mass
c) density   d) viscosity

4 If an aircraft is flying horizontally then its weight must be balanced by the force we call: **(1 mark)**
a) friction   b) mass   c) drag   d) lift

5 Which of these is not a force? **(1 mark)**
a) weight
b) drag
c) lift
d) mass

Score   /5

B — Answer all parts of all questions.

1 The two lists below contain words and their definitions, but they have become muddled. Join the words to their correct definitions.   **(7 marks)**

balanced — An instrument for measuring the size of a force.

newton — A force exerted upon an object placed in a liquid.

upthrust — These forces will have no effect on the motion of an object.

unbalanced — The gravitational force that pulls an object downwards.

newtonmeter — This object can apply forces to other objects without being in contact.

weight — This is the unit we use to measure forces.

magnet — These forces will change the motion of an object.

2 Look at the four diagrams opposite.

A   B   C   D

a) Which skater will have the largest acceleration? .... (1 mark)
b) Which skater will have the second largest acceleration? .... (1 mark)
c) Which skater will have the smallest acceleration? .... (1 mark)
d) Name two other forces that act on the skaters apart from the pushing forces. .... (2 marks)

Score   /12

This is a SATs-style question. Answer all parts of the question.

1 Bill decided to build a newtonmeter of his own. He set up the apparatus shown opposite.

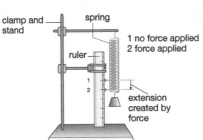

Bill applied forces to his spring and then recorded the length of the spring. His table of results is shown below.

Force in newtons	0	0.5	1.0	1.5	2.0	2.5
Length of spring in centimetres	10.0	12.0	14.0	16.0	17.5	20.0

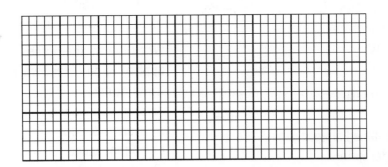

a) Plot a graph of length of spring (*y*-axis) against the force applied (*x*-axis).   (6 marks)

b) Draw in your line of best fit.   (2 marks)

c) Which result did not seem to fit the pattern?... (1 mark)

d) What would be the length of the spring if a force of 0.75 N was applied to it?   (1 mark)

....

e) What force would need to be applied to the spring in order to stretch it to a
length of 15.0 cm? .... (1 mark)

The diagram opposite shows a 5 N weight hanging from a spring.
The spring has stretched by 4.0 cm.

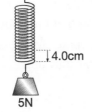

The same force is now applied to two springs identical to
the one above arranged as shown in the diagram opposite.

f) By how much will each spring stretch in this case?.. (1 mark)

Score   /12

Friction and terminal velocity

Whenever an object moves or tries to move, a force will oppose it.
This force is called friction.

A
Choose just one answer, a, b, c or d.

1 Friction can cause an increase in: (1 mark)
   a) weight   b) temperature
   c) height   d) mass

2 Friction between surfaces can be increased by:
   a) polishing the surfaces   (1 mark)
   b) roughening the surfaces
   c) using a lubricant
   d) adding water

3 Dolphins keep their resistance as small as
   possible by: (1 mark)
   a) having a streamlined shape
   b) swimming under water
   c) being mammals   d) being fish

4 As the speed of an object moving through air
   increases, the frictional forces: (1 mark)
   a) increase
   b) decrease
   c) stay the same
   d) act in the direction of the motion.

5 When the friction forces and the driving forces
   applied to an object are equal, the object will
   travel at its: (1 mark)
   a) slowest speed
   b) average speed
   c) normal speed
   d) terminal velocity   Score   /5

B
Answer all parts of all questions.

1 Fill in the missing words.   (10 marks)

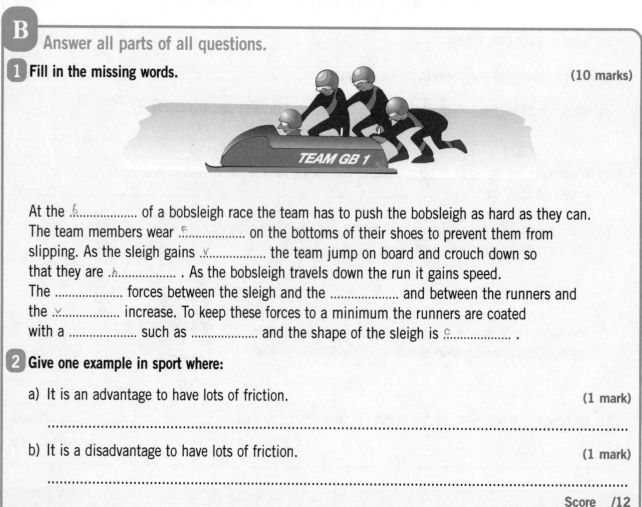

At the .b................. of a bobsleigh race the team has to push the bobsleigh as hard as they can.
The team members wear .f................. on the bottoms of their shoes to prevent them from
slipping. As the sleigh gains .v................. the team jump on board and crouch down so
that they are .b................. . As the bobsleigh travels down the run it gains speed.
The .... forces between the sleigh and the .... and between the runners and
the .v................. increase. To keep these forces to a minimum the runners are coated
with a .... such as .... and the shape of the sleigh is .c................. .

2 Give one example in sport where:

a) It is an advantage to have lots of friction.   (1 mark)

....

b) It is a disadvantage to have lots of friction.   (1 mark)

....

Score   /12

C   These are SATs-style questions. Answer all parts of the questions.

1 The diagram opposite shows a skydiver falling.

a) What force causes the skydiver to fall?   (1 mark)

....

....

b) What happens to the speed of the skydiver immediately after she jumps from the aircraft? (1 mark)

....

....

c) What other force acts on the skydiver as she falls?   (1 mark)

....

....

d) What can you say about the forces acting upon the skydiver when she is falling at her
terminal velocity?   (1 mark)

....

....

e) Explain why the skydiver decelerates immediately after she opens her parachute.   (2 marks)

....

....

2 The diagram opposite shows the brake blocks on
a bicycle.

tyre   tread on
                       tyre

brake blocks

a) Name two things that will happen to the brake
blocks when they are used to slow the bicycle.   (2 marks)

....

....

b) Name one place on a bicycle where oil is used as a lubricant.   (1 mark)

....

Score   /9

How well did you do?   ✗ 1–7 **Try again**   8–12 **Getting there**   13–19 **Good work**   20–26 **Excellent!** ✓

Moments

Forces sometimes make objects turn or rotate. The turning effect of a force is called a moment.

A

Choose just one answer, a, b, c or d.

1 The symbol for a newton metre is: (1 mark)
a) NM   b) nM
c) Nm   d) nm

2 Calculate the moment created when a force of 100 N is applied by a spanner which is 0.4 m long.   (1 mark)
a) 400 Nm   b) 25 Nm
c) 250 Nm   d) 40 Nm

3 How long a spanner is used if a force of 100 N is applied and creates a moment of 25 Nm?
a) 0.5 m   b) 25 m   (1 mark)
c) 5 m   d) 0.25 m

4 If the clockwise moments applied to an object are equal to the anticlockwise moments the object will: (1 mark)
a) turn to the left   b) not turn
c) turn to the right   d) turn clockwise

5 A girl weighing 500 N sits 1.5 m from the centre of a see-saw. Her friend weighs 750 N. How far should she sit from the centre of the see-saw if it is to balance?   (1 mark)
a) 1 m   b) 2 m
c) 1.5 m   d) 0.75 m

Score   /5

B

Answer all parts of all questions. Show all your working for numerical questions.

1 Calculate the size of the moment created by a spanner 0.4 m long when the following forces are applied to it.

a) 10 N. (1 mark)   b) 50 N. (1 mark)

2 Calculate the size of the moment created when a force of 50 N is applied to spanners of the following lengths.

a) 0.3 m (1 mark)   b) 0.7 m (1 mark)   c) 0.2 m (1 mark)

3 Which of the see-saws shown below will:

a) balance?   b) rotate clockwise?   c) rotate anticlockwise?

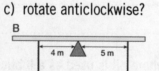
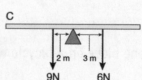

(6 marks)

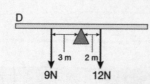
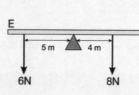
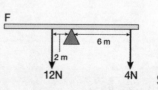

Score   /11

These are SATs-style questions. Answer all parts of the questions.

1 The picture below shows a girl sitting on one end of a plank of wood which has a large crate on the other end.

a) Why is the plank tilted? (2 marks)

....

b) Explain what the girl should do in order to make the plank balance. (1 mark)

....

c) Explain why the action you have described in part b) will balance the plank. (2 marks)

....

2 The diagram below shows the apparatus used by Richard and Clare to investigate the turning effects of forces. They hung weights on their beam and then moved them around until the beam balanced. They then recorded their results in the table shown below.

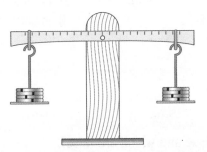

Force in newton	Distance from pivot (cm)	Anticlockwise moment (Ncm)	Force in newtons	Distance from pivot (cm)	Clockwise moment (Ncm)
4	20		5	16	
10	40		20	20	
5	18		3	30	
8	30		5	50	
6	50		10	30	

a) Calculate the moments on each side of the beam. Put your answers into the spaces in the table above. (10 marks)

b) Which result did not fit the pattern? (1 mark)

....

c) What conclusion did Richard and Clare draw from their experiment? (1 mark)

....

Score /17

How well did you do? ✗ 1–11 **Try again**   12–21 **Getting there**   22–27 **Good work**   28–33 **Excellent!** ✓

Pressure

When forces are concentrated over small areas they create large pressures. When forces are spread out over large areas they create small pressures.

A

Choose just one answer, a, b, c or d.

1 Which one of the following is an example of force creating low pressure? **(1 mark)**
a) the point of a drawing pin
b) using a sharp knife
c) someone wearing snowshoes
d) the spikes of a sprinter's shoe

2 What pressure is created when a force of 64 N is applied over an area of 4 m²? **(1 mark)**
a) 256 Pa
b) 16 Nm
c) 16 Pa
d) 256 Nm

3 What force when applied to an area of 10 m² will create a pressure of 5 Pa? **(1 mark)**
a) 2 N
b) 50 N
c) 0.5 N
d) 1 N

4 Over what area must a force of 10 N be applied to create a pressure of 2 Pa? **(1 mark)**
a) 0.5 m²
b) 5 m²
c) 20 m²
d) 0.2 m²

5 The pressure in a liquid **(1 mark)**
a) is the same everywhere
b) increases with depth
c) is greatest from above
d) is caused by air pressure

Score /5

B

Answer all parts of the questions. Show all your working for numerical questions.

1 Which of these statements are true and which are false? **(7 marks)**

a) Thin handles on a carrier bag are a good idea as they create a high pressure, making it easier to carry them. ....

b) Snowshoes spread force over a large area. They therefore create low pressure enabling us to walk over snow without sinking into it. ....

c) The pressure created on a nail when hit by a hammer is greatest on the head of the nail. ....

d) Sharp knives create higher pressures than blunt knives. ....

e) Doing press-ups on the palms of your hands creates the same pressure as doing press-ups on your finger tips. ....

f) Camels have large feet so that they can get a better grip on the sand as they walk through the desert. ....

g) You are more likely to fall through the frozen surface of a lake if you are upright rather than if you are lying on the ice. ....

2 Calculate the pressure created when:

a) a force of 50 N is applied over an area of 25 m². **(1 mark)**
b) a force of 80 N is applied over an area of 16 m². **(1 mark)**
c) a force of 25 N is applied over an area of 2.5 m². **(1 mark)**

B (Continued)

3 Calculate the force that must be applied:

a) over an area of 10 m² to create a pressure of 3 Pa. .... (1 mark)

b) over an area of 4 m² to create a pressure of 5 Pa.. (1 mark)

c) over an area of 16 m² to create a pressure of 1.5 Pa. .... (1 mark)

Score /13

C

These are SATs-style questions. Answer all parts of the questions.

1 The three workmen opposite have just delivered a large crate to the garden of a house. They have been told to leave the crate on the lawn but be careful not to damage the lawn's surface. The crate is very heavy. It weighs 600 N and the workmen are trying to decide which surface they should put in contact with the grass.

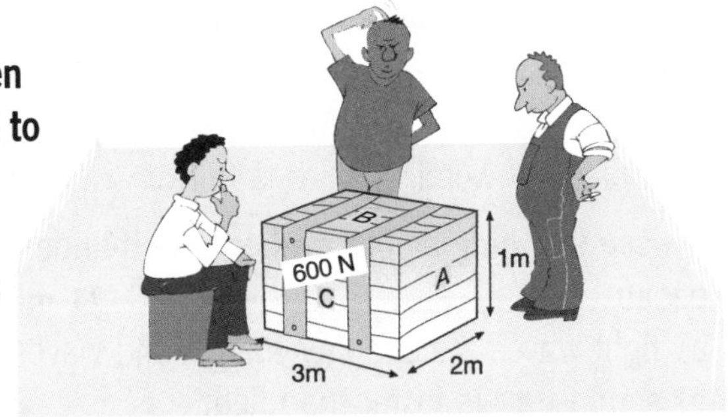

a) Calculate the pressure that would be exerted on the lawn if face A was in contact with the grass. (3 marks)

....

b) Calculate the pressure that would be exerted on the lawn if face B was in contact with the grass. (3 marks)

....

c) Calculate the pressure that would be exerted on the lawn if face C was in contact with the grass. (3 marks)

....

d) Which surface should the crate have in contact with the grass when the workmen leave it? (1 mark)

....

2 The diagram opposite shows a drawing pin.

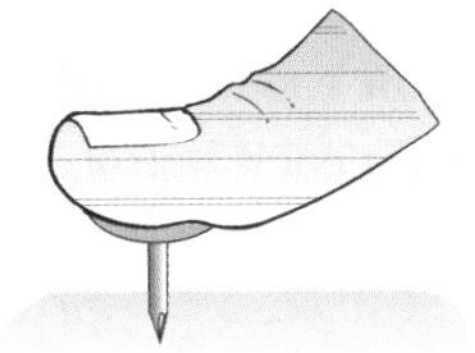

a) Mark with the letter H a place on the diagram where the force applied by the thumb creates a region of high pressure. (1 mark)

b) Mark with the letter L a place on the diagram where the force applied by the thumb creates a region of low pressure. (1 mark)

Score /12

How well did you do? 1–7 Try again 8–13 Getting there 14–22 Good work 23–30 Excellent!

For more help on this topic see KS3 Science Success Guide pages 96–97

Light rays and reflection

Rays of light travel in straight lines. We see most objects because of the light they reflect.

A Choose just one answer, a, b, c or d.

1 A luminous object: (1 mark)
a) reflects light   b) refracts light
c) gives off light   d) diffracts light

2 Which of these is an example of a transparent object? (1 mark)
a) a brick   b) a pane of glass
c) a piece of wood   d) a mirror

3 We see lightning before we hear the thunder because: (1 mark)
a) light waves are stronger than sound waves
b) sound travels faster than light
c) light travels faster than sound
d) sound waves are stronger than light waves

4 A ray of light strikes the surface of a plane mirror with an angle of incidence of 60°. What is its angle of reflection? (1 mark)
a) 30°   b) 10°
c) 90°   d) 60°

5 An optical instrument that contains two mirrors and can be used to look over high walls is called a: (1 mark)
a) kaleidoscope
b) telescope
c) microscope
d) periscope

Score   /5

B Answer all parts of all questions.

1 Fill in the missing words. (14 marks)

We can see through a pane of glass because glass is a .... material.
We cannot see through a sheet of steel because steel is an .... material.
If we place an .... object in front of a source of light we can create a ....
An object that emits light like a .... is called a .... object. We see .... - .... objects because of the .... they reflect.

Shadows have the same .... as the objects that create them. This suggests that .... travels in .... Light waves travel much .... than sound waves. This is why we always see lightning before we .... the ....

2 The diagrams below show rays of light striking plane mirrors. Draw in accurately the reflected ray for each mirror. (4 marks)

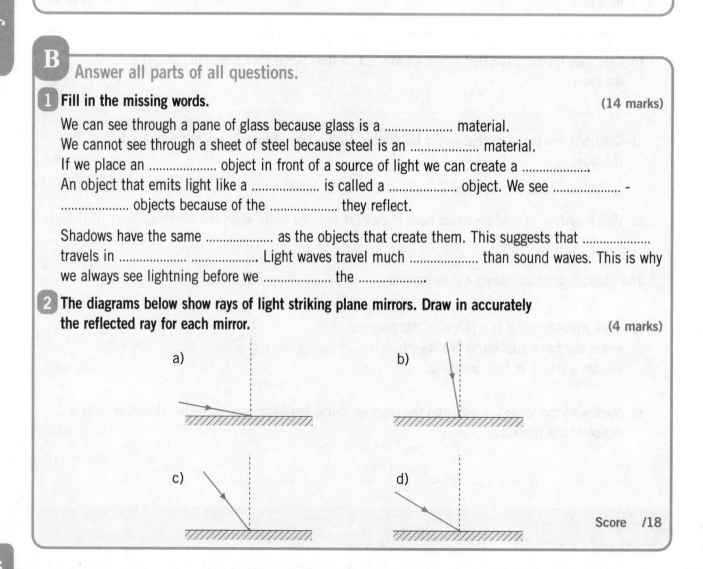

a)

b)

c)

d)

Score   /18

C These are SATs-style questions. Answer all parts of the questions.

1 The picture below shows two children playing 'pin the tail on the donkey'.

a) Name one luminous object you can see in the diagram.   (1 mark)

....

b) Name one non-luminous object you can see in the diagram.   (1 mark)

....

c) Why is Sally unable to see where she must pin the tail on the donkey?   (1 mark)

....

d) Draw rays of light on the picture above showing how David is able to see the
   picture of the donkey.   (2 marks)

....

2 The picture below shows a boy standing 2 m from a plane mirror. The boy is 1.5 m tall.

a) How far behind the mirror is the boy's image?   (1 mark)

....

b) Is the boy's image in the mirror less than 1.5 m tall, 1.5 m tall or more than 1.5 m tall? (1 mark)

....

c) The image of the boy is laterally inverted. Explain what this phrase means.   (2 marks)

....

Score   /9

How well did you do?   ✗ 0–8 **Try again**   9–16 **Getting there**   17–24 **Good work**   25–32 **Excellent!** ✓

Refraction and colour

Rays of light travel at different speeds in different media. When they cross the boundary between two media the change in speed may cause them to change direction. This is called refraction.

A Choose just one answer, a, b, c or d.

1 When a ray of light enters a glass block it:
a) slows down **(1 mark)**
b) speeds up
c) bends away from the normal
d) spreads out

2 The splitting of white light into the colours of the rainbow by a prism is called: **(1 mark)**
a) dispersion
b) refraction
c) total internal reflection
d) resonance

3 What colour(s) is (are) reflected by a blue car in white light? **(1 mark)**
a) red   b) green
c) all colours   d) blue

4 What colour(s) is (are) reflected by a white car in white light? **(1 mark)**
a) none   b) blue
c) green   d) all

5 What colour light can pass through a red filter?
a) none   b) all   **(1 mark)**
c) red   d) blue

Score   /5

B Answer all parts of all questions.

1 When white light hits a green object, all the colours are absorbed except for green, which is reflected. This is why the object looks green.

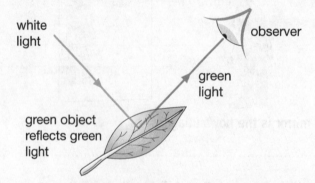

white light

observer

green light

green object reflects green light

Draw diagrams and write a few sentences to explain the appearance of each of the following when seen in white light.

a) a red ball   **(3 marks)**

b) a blue box   **(3 marks)**

c) a white sheet of paper   **(3 marks)**

d) a black cat   **(3 marks)**

B (Continued)

2 **Write out a definition of each of the following.**   (7 marks)

a) refraction   ....

b) normal   ....

c) medium   ....

d) dispersion   ....

e) spectrum   ....

f) dye   ....

g) coloured filter   ....

Score   /19

C   These are SATs-style questions. Answer all parts of the questions.

1 **The diagram below shows a ray of light striking the surface of a glass block.**

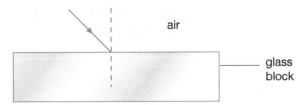

a) Using a pencil and ruler, draw on the diagram above to show what happens
    to the ray of light after it has struck the surface of the glass block.   (3 marks)

b) In the space below show what happens to a ray of light which strikes the
    block at an angle of 90° to its surface.   (1 mark)

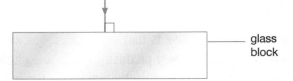

c) How fast are the rays of light travelling when they are inside the glass
    compared with their speed in air?   (1 mark)
    ....

2 **The diagram below shows white light passing through a prism, producing a band of coloured light.**

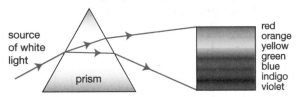

a) What is the name given to this band of colours?   (1 mark)
    ....

b) Name one natural phenomenon which also produces a band of colours.   (1 mark)
    ....

c) A student looks at the band of colours through a red filter. Describe what she sees. ....(1 mark)

Score   /8

How well did you do?   ✗ 0–8 **Try again**   9–16 **Getting there**   17–24 **Good work**   25–32 **Excellent!** ✓

For more help on this topic see KS3 Science Success Guide pages 100–101

Sounds

All sounds begin with an object that is vibrating. The vibrations travel outwards from the source as waves.

A Choose just one answer, a, b, c or d.

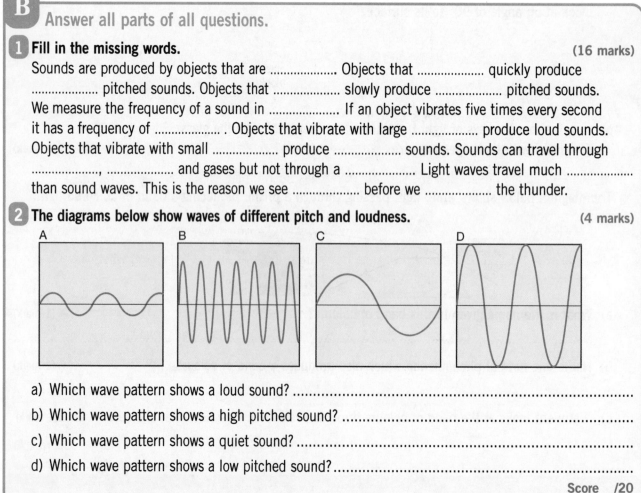

1 Large objects vibrate slowly and produce what kind of notes? **(1 mark)**
a) low pitch   b) high pitch
c) loud   d) quiet

2 Objects that vibrate with large amplitudes produce what kind of sounds? **(1 mark)**
a) high pitch   b) quiet
c) low pitch   d) loud

3 We measure the frequency of a wave in:

(1 mark)
a) metres   b) hertz
c) metres per second d) hertz per second

4 Through which of these can sound NOT travel?
(1 mark)
a) wood   b) water
c) vacuum   d) air

5 Which part of our bodies is made to vibrate by sound waves? **(1 mark)**
a) nerve cells
b) brain
c) vocal chords
d) eardrum

Score   /5

B Answer all parts of all questions.

1 Fill in the missing words.   (16 marks)

Sounds are produced by objects that are .... Objects that .... quickly produce .... pitched sounds. Objects that .... slowly produce .... pitched sounds. We measure the frequency of a sound in .... If an object vibrates five times every second it has a frequency of .... Objects that vibrate with large .... produce loud sounds. Objects that vibrate with small .... produce .... sounds. Sounds can travel through ...., ... and gases but not through a .... Light waves travel much .... than sound waves. This is the reason we see .... before we .... the thunder.

2 The diagrams below show waves of different pitch and loudness.   (4 marks)

A   B   C   D

a) Which wave pattern shows a loud sound? ....
b) Which wave pattern shows a high pitched sound? ....
c) Which wave pattern shows a quiet sound? ....
d) Which wave pattern shows a low pitched sound? ....

Score   /20

C

1 Linda is standing watching a firework display.

a) Explain why Linda sees the rocket explode and then hears the explosion some time later. (2 marks)

....

....

....

b) What happens to some of the light when it hits the surface of the lake? (1 mark)

....

2 The diagram opposite shows an electric bell inside an air-tight jar.

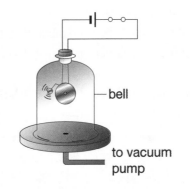

a) What does John hear when the switch is closed? (1 mark)

....

b) Explain how this sound travels to John. (2 marks)

....

c) What does John hear after the vacuum pump has been turned on and all the air removed from the jar? (1 mark)

....

d) Explain the difference between what he hears when there is air in the jar, and when there is no air in the jar. (2 marks)

....

....

e) John says light waves can travel through a vacuum. How does he know this? (1 mark)

....

Score   /10

Echoes and hearing

When sound waves strike a hard surface they are reflected. This reflected sound is called an echo.

A   Choose just one answer, a, b, c or d.

1 Loudness is measured in: (1 mark)
a) decibels   b) cycles per second
c) hertz   d) centimetres

2 Sound waves used for finding the distance of an object are called: (1 mark)
a) RADAR   b) GOCAR
c) ECHOAR   d) SONAR

3 What is ultrasound?   (1 mark)
a) sound we can't hear because it has too high a frequency
b) sound we can't hear because it is too quiet
c) sound we can't hear because it is travelling too fast
d) sound we can't hear because it has too low a frequency

4 What is the hearing range of an average person?   (1 mark)
a) 20 – 20 000 Hz
b) 0 – 25 000 Hz
c) 20 – 2000 Hz
d) 25 – 2500 Hz

5 What level on the decibel scale would the noise from nearby aircraft taking off reach?   (1 mark)
a) 20 dB
b) 80 dB
c) 200 dB
d) 120 dB

Score   /5

B   Answer all parts of all questions.

1 The letters of the words below have become jumbled up. Rearrange the letters, then write a sentence that explains the meaning of each word(s).   (8 marks)

a) soheecs   e...
b) rason   s...
c) ssuuntlador   u...
d) rraaggeennhi   h...............r...
e) eeetdlfrc   r...
f) eeelldiccbas   d............s...
g) ssunoeld   l...
h) eeeerrafddns   e............d...

2 We measure the loudness of sounds on the decibel scale. An axis for the decibel scale has been drawn opposite.

Add the following sounds or sources of sound to the decibel scale to indicate their loudness.

a) complete silence   b) normal conversation
c) noisy machinery in a factory   d) a small bird singing
e) a jet aircraft taking off   f) someone whispering.

(6 marks)

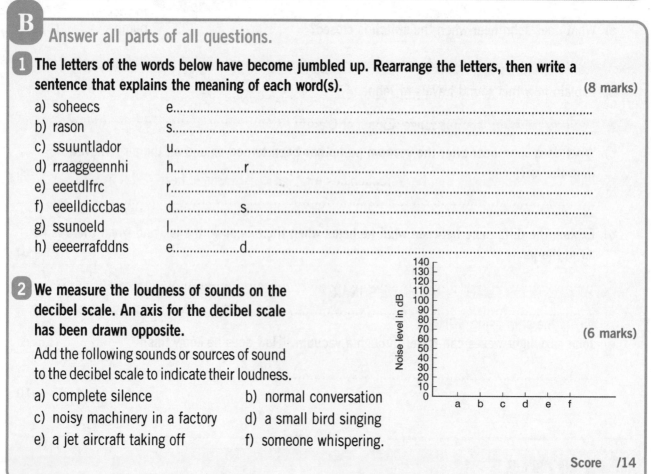

Score   /14

C   These are SATs-style questions. Answer all parts of the questions.

1 Emma and Clare are testing each other's audible range. They are using a piece of apparatus called a signal generator to produce sounds of different frequencies.

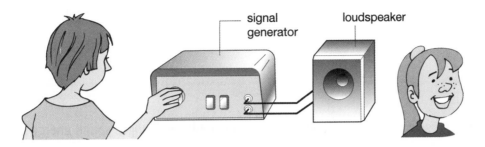

signal generator   loudspeaker

Emma goes first. Clare sets the frequency of the signal generator at 0 Hz and then gradually increases it. Emma tells Clare immediately when she is able to hear the sound. Clare records the frequency of the note. Clare then increases the frequency of the note until Emma tells her she can no longer hear it. Clare records the frequency of this note. The two girls then repeat the whole experiment, but this time Emma tests Clare's audible range.

The results of the two experiments are shown in the table below.

	Lowest frequency heard in Hz	Highest frequency heard in Hz
Emma	19	20 500
Clare	18	20 100

a) Explain in your own words the meaning of the phrase audible range.   (2 marks)

....

b) What was the lowest frequency that Emma could hear?   (1 mark)

....

c) What was the highest frequency Clare could hear?   (1 mark)

....

d) Who had the wider audible range, Emma or Clare?   (1 mark)

....

e) What do we call sounds that have frequencies too high for humans to hear?   (1 mark)

....

f) Name two animals that can hear sounds with too high a frequency for humans to hear.   (2 marks)

....

2 The picture opposite shows a ship using SONAR.

a) Why is the ship using SONAR?   (1 mark)

....

b) What is an echo?   (1 mark)

....

Score   /10

How well did you do?   ✗ 1–8 **Try again**   9–14 **Getting there**   15–21 **Good work**   22–29 **Excellent!** ✓

For more help on this topic see KS3 Science Success Guide pages 104–105

Energy

We all need energy to be able to do things. We get this energy from the food we eat. Food is a form of chemical energy, but there are other sources and forms of energy.

A Choose just one answer, a, b, c or d.

1 Which of the following is not a type of stored energy? **(1 mark)**
   a) chemical   b) gravitational
   c) elastic potential   potential
   d) sound

2 What kind of energy is stored in a battery?
   a) nuclear   b) light   **(1 mark)**
   c) chemical   d) heat

3 The energy stored in a stretched catapult is:
   (1 mark)
   a) kinetic energy   b) elastic potential
   energy
   c) heat energy   d) chemical energy

4 A microphone changes sound energy into:
   (1 mark)
   a) thermal energy
   b) gravitational potential energy
   c) electrical energy
   d) light energy

5 A wind turbine changes what kind of energy into electrical energy? **(1 mark)**
   a) kinetic energy
   b) chemical energy
   c) sound energy
   d) gravitational potential energy

Score   /5

B Answer all parts of all questions.

1 Draw a line connecting each word to the correct explanation. The first one has been done for you.
(9 marks)

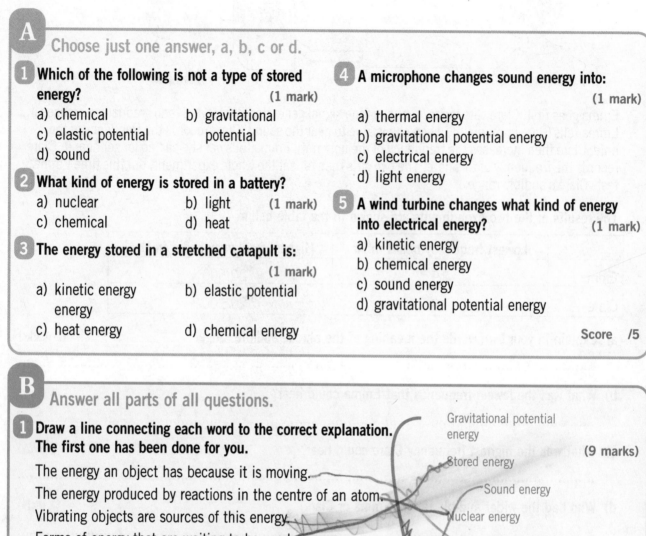

The energy an object has because it is moving.
The energy produced by reactions in the centre of an atom.
Vibrating objects are sources of this energy.
Forms of energy that are waiting to be used.
Food is an example of this.
This energy is available every time a current flows.
Winding up a spring will give it this type of energy.
Most of our energy on the Earth begins as this.
When one type of energy changes into another type of energy.
The energy an object has when it is high up.

Gravitational potential energy
Stored energy
Sound energy
Nuclear energy
Electrical energy
Kinetic energy
Chemical energy
Elastic potential energy
Light energy
Energy transfer

2 Put the words in each of the groups below into the correct order. **(5 marks)**

a) into candle energy energy and chemical light heat burning changes a.

....

b) sound a energy changes loudspeaker electrical into.

....

c) stores energy a battery chemical.

....

B (Continued)

d) kinetic water is has flowing energy which.

....

e) potential of all stored and are chemical, potential forms elastic gravitational energy energy energy energy.

....

Score /14

C

These are SATs-style questions. Answer all parts of the questions.

1 The pictures below show energy changes taking place.

a   b   c

battery

Fill in the missing words in the sentences below.

a) The car is changing .... energy into .... energy and .... energy. (3 marks)

b) The CD player and loudspeakers are changing .... energy into .... energy and .... energy. (3 marks)

c) The light bulb is changing .... energy into .... energy and .... energy. (3 marks)

2 a) Which piece of apparatus would you use:

i)   to change sound energy into electrical energy? (1 mark)

....

ii) to change elastic potential energy into kinetic energy? (1 mark)

....

iii) to change chemical energy into electrical energy? (1 mark)

....

b) Where do animals get their energy from? (1 mark)

....

c) Where do plants get their energy from? (1 mark)

....

3 Explain in your own words the energy changes that take place when:

a) water evaporates from a lake, rises and forms clouds. (2 marks)

....

b) water falls as rain on a mountain and then runs down the mountainside back into the lake. (2 marks)

....

Score /18

How well did you do?   ✗ 1–7 **Try again**   8–18 **Getting there**   19–28 **Good work**   29–37 **Excellent!** ✓

Using energy resources

Fossil fuels are one of our most concentrated sources of energy. We use a large amount of fossil fuels to generate our electricity.

A Choose just one answer, a, b, c or d.

1 Which of these is not a fossil fuel? (1 mark)
- a) wood
- b) oil
- c) coal
- d) gas

2 Which gas causes the problem we call the 'Greenhouse effect'? (1 mark)
- a) air
- b) carbon dioxide
- c) oxygen
- d) nitrogen

3 Burning which fuel produces gases that cause acid rain? (1 mark)
- a) wood
- b) coal
- c) gas
- d) methane

4 Which of the following will not make fossil fuels last longer? (1 mark)
- a) improving heat insulation in the home
- b) using more public transport
- c) developing more efficient car engines
- d) driving bigger cars

5 The steam produced in a power station is used to: (1 mark)
- a) heat turbines
- b) warm water
- c) lubricate transformers
- d) turn turbines

Score /5

B Answer all parts of all questions.

1 Fill in the missing words in the sentences below. (13 marks)

Coal, oil and .... are .... fuels. They are concentrated .... of energy. They are formed from the remains of .... and .... that died millions of years ago. But instead of rotting they became covered with many layers of .... As a result they were under great .... and they were at high .... These conditions changed them into .... fuels. Because these fuels take a long time to form they are called .... fuels. Once they have been used up they cannot be .... Burning these fuels can cause problems to the environment such as .... and the ....

2 The letters of the words below have become jumbled up. Rearrange the letters then write a sentence that explains the meaning of the words. (7 marks)

a) sssfflloeui

....

b) oottnaprewsi

....

c) iiaadrcn

....

d) eeeeefftuoghncrs

....

e) oponilltu

....

f) eeeanrlbw

....

g) nnneeebolawr

....

Score /20

C These are SATs-style questions. Answer all parts of the questions.

1 The diagram below shows the energy changes that take place in a power station using natural gas for its fuel.

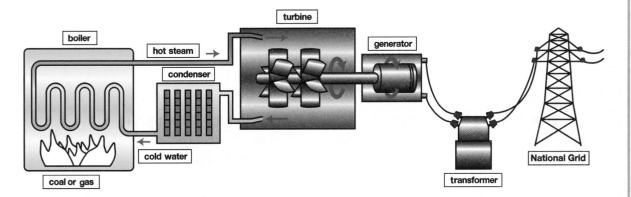

a) What kind of energy is stored in natural gas? (1 mark)

....

b) How is the energy stored in natural gas released? (1 mark)

....

c) What is the energy released from the natural gas used for in a power station? (1 mark)

....

d) What energy transfer takes place when the steam enters the turbine housing? (2 marks)

....

e) What energy transfer takes place when the turbine turns the generator? (2 marks)

....

2 Natural gas is a fossil fuel.

a) Name two other types of fossil fuel. (2 marks)

....

b) Why are fossil fuels called non-renewable sources of energy? (1 mark)

....

c) Name two types of environmental problems that may arise because of the use of fossil fuels in our power stations. (2 marks)

....

d) Suggest two ways in which we could make fossil fuels last longer. (2 marks)

....

Score   /14

How well did you do? 1–9 **Try again**   10–19 **Getting there**   20–29 **Good work**   30–39 **Excellent!** ✓

Alternative sources of energy

Burning fossil fuels in large quantities creates many environmental problems. One way to reduce these problems is to use alternative sources of energy.

A

Choose just one answer, a, b, c or d.

1 Which of the following is not a renewable source of energy? **(1 mark)**
a) waves b) wind
c) oil d) solar

2 Which of the following does not have a high initial cost? **(1 mark)**
a) hydroelectricity b) biomass
c) tidal energy d) geothermal energy

3 Which of the following uses the energy stored in living matter? **(1 mark)**
a) solar energy b) wind energy
c) biomass d) tidal energy

4 Which of the following does not make use of kinetic energy? **(1 mark)**
a) wind energy
b) tidal energy
c) hydroelectricity
d) solar energy

5 The energy possessed by water trapped behind a dam or barrage is: **(1 mark)**
a) gravitational potential energy
b) elastic potential energy
c) kinetic energy
d) chemical energy

Score /5

B

Answer all parts of all questions.

1 The three lists below contain the names of alternative sources of energy, their advantages and their disadvantages. Draw a line from the name of the source of energy to a) the correct advantage and b) the correct disadvantage. **(10 marks)**

Advantages	Energy source	Disadvantages
Reliable, two tides per day	geothermal	Obstacle to water transport
Low level technology	tidal	Poor energy capture
Useful for isolated islands	wind	Possible visual and noise pollution
No pollution or environmental problems	hydroelectric	Very few suitable sites
Energy can be stored until required	wave	High cost to environment, i.e. flooding

2 Fill in the missing words in the sentences below. **(5 marks)**

The .... energy stored in things that have grown such as .... can be released by burning. The original source of this energy is the .... Because this source of energy can be continually replaced it is called a .... of ....

Score /15

C

This is a SATs-style question. Answer all parts of the question.

1 a) Name one non-renewable fuel. (1 mark)

....

b) Name one renewable fuel. (1 mark)

....

c) Name two alternative sources of energy which depend directly on the weather conditions, i.e. if the conditions are not correct they produce no energy. (2 marks)

....

d) Name two alternative sources of energy that are unaffected by weather conditions. (2 marks)

....

The diagram opposite shows a geothermal power station.

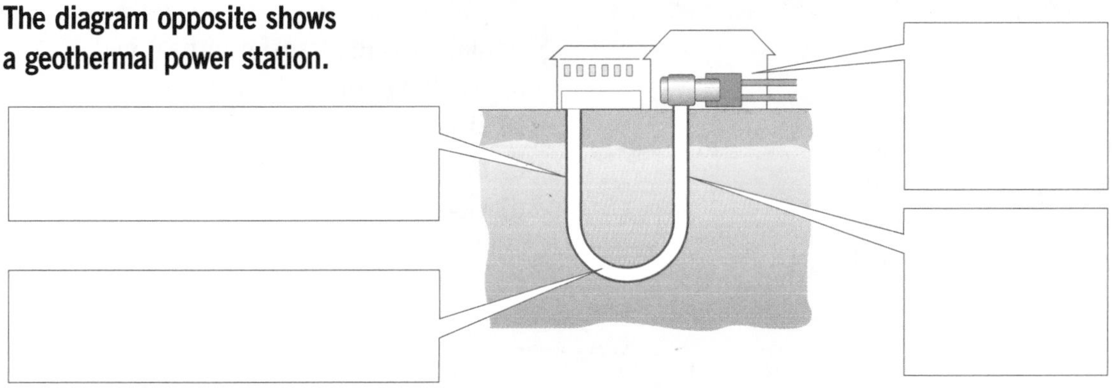

e) Fill in each of the labels to explain how electricity is generated by a geothermal power station. (4 marks)

....

The diagram opposite shows a simple hydroelectric power station.

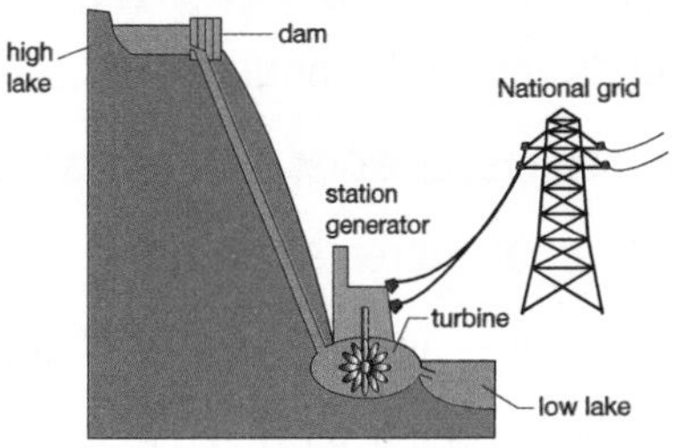
high lake
dam
National grid
station generator
turbine
low lake

f) Fill in the block diagram below showing the energy changes that take place when electricity is generated. (4 marks)

....

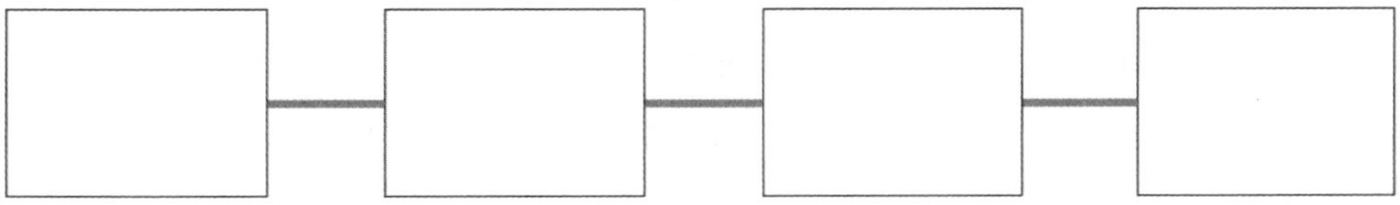

g) Explain in your own words why the water in the high lake has stored energy. (1 mark)

....

Score /15

How well did you do? ✗ 1–9 Try again 10–19 Getting there 20–27 Good work 28–35 Excellent! ✓

For more help on this topic see KS3 Science Success Guide pages 106–111

Heat transfer

Heat flows when there is a temperature difference between two places. It flows from the hotter to the cooler place. Three methods by which it can do this are conduction, convection and radiation.

A

Choose just one answer, a, b, c or d.

1 **Heat is transferred along a metal rod by:**
(1 mark)
a) convection   b) radiation
c) conduction   d) nuclear power

2 **Conduction transfers heat by:** (1 mark)
a) vibrations   b) chemical reactions
c) electric currents   d) rays

3 **Woven materials such as wool and cotton are excellent insulators because:** (1 mark)
a) they contain trapped air
b) they are natural materials
c) they are man-made materials
d) they are soft

4 **Transfer of heat by convection cannot take place in:** (1 mark)
a) liquids
b) gases
c) fluids
d) solids

5 **Radiation is the transfer of heat by:** (1 mark)
a) electric currents
b) radioactive materials
c) rays
d) vibrations

Score   /5

B

Answer all parts of all questions.

1 **Which of the following statements are true and which are false?** (12 marks)

a) Metals are good conductors of heat. ....

b) Saucepans have plastic handles because plastics are good conductors of heat. ....

c) Convection currents can move heat in solids and liquids. ....

d) Houses are painted white in hot countries in order to reflect radiation and so stay cool. ....

e) Even with double glazing, heat can escape through a window by radiation. ....

f) Heat energy travels to the Earth from the Sun by conduction. ....

g) The particles at the hot end of a metal rod vibrate vigorously. ....

h) Woven materials such as wool and cotton contain trapped air and so are excellent insulators. ....

i) Plastic table mats are good insulators. They prevent heat from hot food reaching and damaging the table top. ....

j) A thick piece of glass is a better insulator than two thin ones with a layer of air between them. ....

k) When fluids are heated they become less dense and fall. ....

l) A black car will absorb more radiation than a white car and will therefore remain cooler. ....

Score   /12

These are SATs-style questions. Answer all parts of the questions.

1 The diagram opposite shows the apparatus being used by two pupils, Katy and Richard.

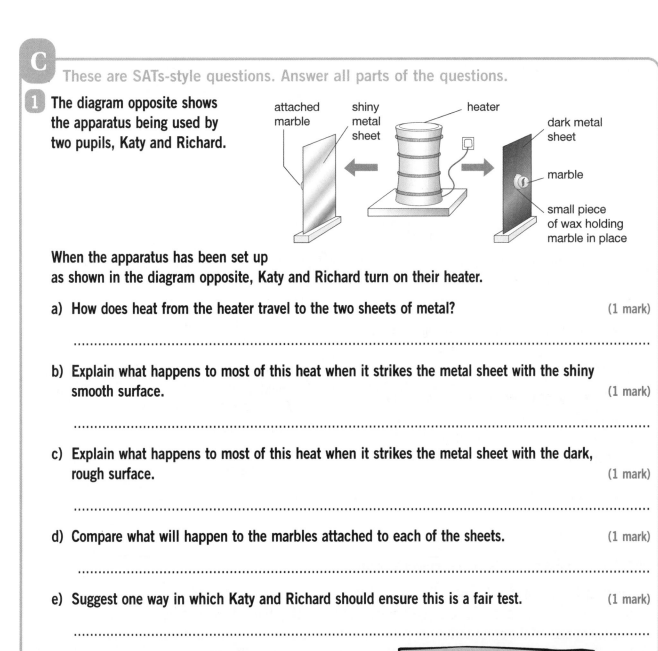

attached marble · shiny metal sheet · heater · dark metal sheet · marble · small piece of wax holding marble in place

When the apparatus has been set up as shown in the diagram opposite, Katy and Richard turn on their heater.

a) How does heat from the heater travel to the two sheets of metal? (1 mark)

....

b) Explain what happens to most of this heat when it strikes the metal sheet with the shiny smooth surface. (1 mark)

....

c) Explain what happens to most of this heat when it strikes the metal sheet with the dark, rough surface. (1 mark)

....

d) Compare what will happen to the marbles attached to each of the sheets. (1 mark)

....

e) Suggest one way in which Katy and Richard should ensure this is a fair test. (1 mark)

....

2 The picture opposite shows a house that has not been insulated.

Suggest 5 ways in which the owners of this house could reduce heat loss. (5 marks)

....
....
....
....
....

Score /10

How well did you do? ✗ 1–7 **Try again** 8–12 **Getting there** 13–19 **Good work** 20–27 **Excellent!** ✓

Circuit components

Instead of drawing actual components we use circuit diagrams with easy to draw symbols.

A
Choose just one answer, a, b, c or d.

1 An electric current is a flow of: (1 mark)
a) atoms
b) charge
c) neutrons
d) volts

2 Charges can be made to move using: (1 mark)
a) wires
b) resistors
c) cells
d) switches

3 What are charges given as they pass through batteries? (1 mark)
a) energy
b) more charge
c) insulation
d) resistance

4 Switches turn circuits on and off by making them:
a) hot or cold (1 mark)
b) conductors or insulators
c) positive or negative
d) complete or incomplete

5 To adjust the brightness of a bulb in a circuit we could use: (1 mark)
a) a switch
b) a variable resistor
c) a connecting wire
d) an insulator

Score   /5

B
Answer all parts of all questions.

1 Fill in the missing words in the sentences below. (10 marks)

An electric current is a flow of .... The .... are given energy and made to flow using a .... or a .... Charges can flow easily through connecting .... The wires and all the other components make a loop called a .... If there are no gaps the loop is called a .... If there are gaps it is called an ....

Drawing the actual components in a circuit is difficult. Instead we use .... which contain easy to draw .... for the components.

2 The names of some common circuit components and their symbols are shown below. Draw a line connecting the name of each component with its circuit symbol. The first one has been done for you.

Bulb (7 marks)

Cell

Open switch

Variable resistor

Buzzer

Resistor

Battery

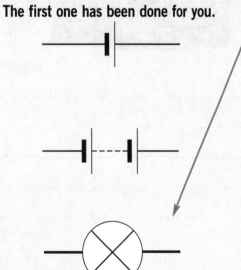
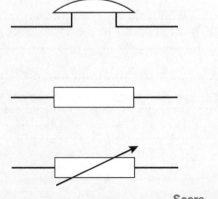

Score   /17

C

1 Linda and Julie have built the circuit shown opposite. They are going to use it to test different materials in order to discover if they are conductors or insulators.

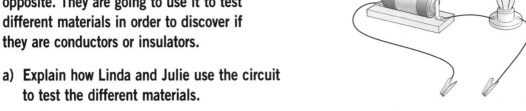

a) Explain how Linda and Julie use the circuit to test the different materials.   (3 marks)

....

....

The table below shows some of the materials the two students tested.

Material	Conductor	Insulator
copper	✔	
steel		
paper		
bronze		
graphite		
mercury		

b) Put a tick in the second column if you think the material is a conductor and in the third column if you think the material is an insulator. The first one has been done for you.   (5 marks)

Linda and Julie build a second circuit similar to the one shown opposite.

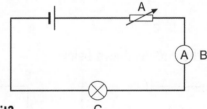

c) What is the name of component A in the above circuit?   (1 mark)

....

d) What is the name of component B in the above circuit?   (1 mark)

....

e) What happens to the reading on component B if the value of A is increased?   (1 mark)

....

f) What is the name of component C in the above circuit?   (1 mark)

....

g) What happens to the appearance of component C if the value of component A is increased?   (1 mark)

....

h) Give one practical use of the above circuit.   (1 mark)

....

Score   /14

Circuits: current and voltage

Currents carry energy around a circuit. They receive this energy from a cell or battery and then give it away to the different components in the circuit.

A Choose just one answer, a, b, c or d.

1 A series circuit has no: (1 mark)
a) gaps   b) cell
c) resistor   d) branches

2 The current in a series circuit: (1 mark)
a) gets smaller as it moves away from the cell or battery
b) always flows clockwise
c) gets bigger as it moves away from the cell or battery
d) is the same everywhere

3 Current is measured with a: (1 mark)
a) voltmeter   b) variable resistor
c) ammeter   d) battery

4 A voltmeter connected across a cell measures: (1 mark)
a) the temperature of the charges as they pass through the cell
b) the energy given to the charges as they pass through the cell
c) the polarity of the cell
d) the current flowing through the cell

5 When electric current passes through a buzzer electrical energy is changed into: (1 mark)
a) heat and light energy
b) sound energy
c) light energy
d) elastic strain energy   Score /5

B Answer all parts of all questions.

1 Look at the circuits drawn below.   (4 marks)

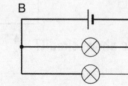
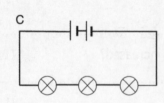
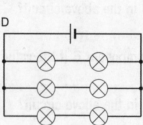
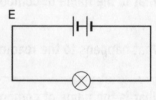

a) Name one of the above circuits that is a series circuit. ....

b) In which circuit does the bulb glow most brightly? ....

c) In which circuits are there batteries? ....

d) In which circuit can a switch be used to turn three bulbs on and off? ....

2 a) What is the name of the instrument we use to measure the current flowing in a circuit? .... (1 mark)

b) In what units do we measure electric current? .... (1 mark)

Score /6

C

These are SATs-style questions. Answer all parts of the questions.

1 The diagram below shows a circuit containing 3 switches and 4 bulbs.

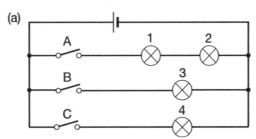

a) Which bulbs glow when switch A is closed and switches B and C are open? (2 marks)

....

b) Which bulbs glow when switches A and B are closed and switch C is open? (3 marks)

....

c) Which switch(es) must be closed if bulb 4 is to glow and bulbs 1, 2 and 3 are to remain off? (2 marks)

....

2 The diagram opposite shows a circuit containing a cell, a switch, two ammeters and a bulb.

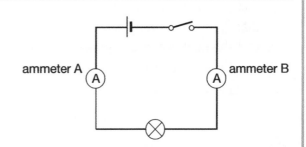

When the switch is closed the reading on ammeter A is 0.1A.

What is the reading on ammeter B?   More than 0.1 A   0.1 A   Less than 0.1 A
(Tick the correct answer)   (1 mark)

3 The diagram opposite shows a circuit containing a cell, a switch, three ammeters, a resistor and a bulb.

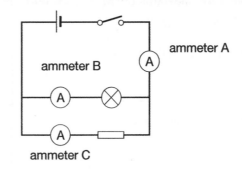

When the switch is closed the reading on ammeter A is 0.6 A. The reading on ammeter B is 0.4 A.

a) What is the reading on ammeter C? (1 mark)

....

b) What energy transfer takes place when current passes through a bulb? (3 marks)

....

c) What energy transfer takes place when current passes through a resistor? (2 marks)

....

Score   /14

How well did you do?   1–6 Try again   7–12 **Getting there**   13–20 **Good work**   21–25 **Excellent!** ✓

Magnets and electromagnets

Magnets attract magnetic materials. Electromagnets made from coils of wire and soft iron cores also attract magnetic materials.

A
Choose just one answer, a, b, c or d.

1 Which of the following is a magnetic material?
a) paper   b) plastic   **(1 mark)**
c) steel   d) brass

2 Which of the following is a non-magnetic material?   **(1 mark)**
a) copper   b) iron
c) nickel   d) steel

3 If the lines of a magnetic field are close together this shows: **(1 mark)**
a) that the field is weak here
b) that the field is strong here
c) that the field is changing direction
d) that there is no magnetic field here

4 Give one advantage of an electromagnet compared with a permanent magnet.   **(1 mark)**
a) it is smaller
b) it can be turned on and off
c) it is quicker to use
d) it creates less pollution

5 Which one of the following will not increase the strength of an electromagnet?   **(1 mark)**
a) using a larger current
b) adding more turns
c) using thicker wire
d) adding a soft iron core

Score   /5

B
Answer all parts of all questions.

1 Complete the diagrams below to show how the molecular magnets in the domains of a magnetic material are arranged: **(2 marks)**

a) when it is unmagnetised

b) when it is magnetised

2 Complete the diagram below to show the shape of the magnetic field around a bar magnet.   **(1 mark)**

Score   /3

C

These are SATs-style questions. Answer all parts of the questions.

1 The diagram opposite shows a simple electromagnet.

a) Add lines of force to the diagram opposite to show
    the shape of the magnetic field around
    the electromagnet.   (3 marks)

b) Give two ways in which the strength of
    an electromagnet can be increased.   (2 marks)

....

....

c) Give one advantage of an electromagnet over a permanent magnet.   (1 mark)

....

....

2 The diagram below shows the circuit used for an electric bell. Explain in detail what happens when
the bell-push is pressed.   (4 marks)

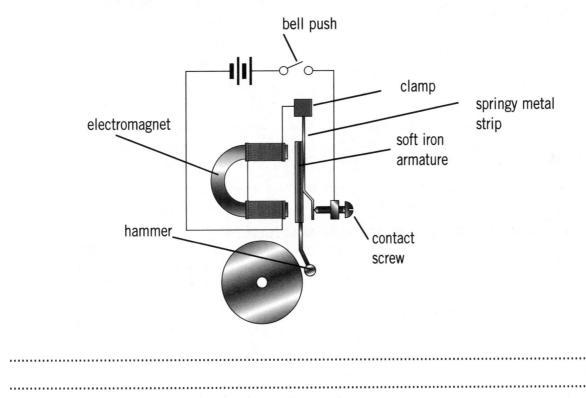

....

....

....

....

Score   /10

How well did you do?   ✗ 1–4 **Try again**   5–9 **Getting there**   10–13 **Good work**   14–18 **Excellent!** ✓

The Solar System 1

Our planet is rotating and at the same time orbiting the Sun. There are a total of nine planets in our Solar System.

A Choose just one answer, a, b, c or d.

1 We experience day and night on the Earth because: (1 mark)
a) the Earth is spinning
b) the Earth is tilted
c) the Earth is round
d) the Moon orbits the Earth

2 When we in the UK are having our winter: (1 mark)
a) the northern part of the Earth is tilted away from the Sun
b) the southern part of the Earth is tilted away from the Sun
c) people in Australia are also having their winter
d) the Sun's path goes high across the sky

3 When a part of the Earth is facing away from the Sun: (1 mark)
a) It is winter here
b) It is daytime here
c) It is summer here
d) It is night time here

4 We can see stars like the Sun because (1 mark)
a) they are not far away
b) they reflect light
c) they emit light
d) they are big

5 99% of the mass of our Solar System (1 mark)
a) is contained in the planets
b) is contained in the Sun
c) is contained in the asteroid belt
d) is contained in the moons of our Solar System

Score /5

B Answer all parts of all questions.

1 How many of the following can you find in the word search? (11 marks)

a) luminous objects ....
b) Non-luminous object that orbits the Earth ....
c) Objects like the Earth that orbit the Sun ....
d) Large lumps of rocks that orbit the Sun ....
e) Two seasons ....and ....
f) The part of the sky where the Sun sets ....
g) The part of the sky where the Sun rises ....
h) It is because the Earth does this that we have seasons ....
i) One complete rotation of a planet is a ....
j) One complete orbit of the Sun by a planet is called a ....

P	L	A	N	E	T	S
E	A	S	T	D	I	T
S	B	T	X	Y	L	A
U	C	E	M	E	T	R
M	Y	R	O	A	S	S
M	T	O	O	R	G	O
E	W	I	N	T	E	R
R	N	D	A	Y	L	N
A	U	S	W	E	S	T

These are SATs-style questions. Answer all parts of the questions.

1 The table below contains information about the planets in our Solar System.

Planet	Distance from the Sun (millions of km)	Orbit time in Earth years	Mass compared with the Earth	Surface temp. in °C
Mercury	60	0.2	0.05	350
Venus	110	0.6	0.8	—
Earth	150	1.0	1.0	22
Mars	230	1.9	0.1	–30
Jupiter	775	11.9	318.0	–150
Saturn	1450	29.5	95.0	—
Uranus	2900	84.0	15.0	–210
Neptune	4500	165.0	17.0	—
Pluto	5900	248.0	0.1	–230

a) Which planet in our Solar System has the largest mass?

....

b) Which two planets are closer to the Sun than to the Earth?

....

c) How long does it take for Uranus to orbit the Sun?

....

d) Which planet has a surface temperature only slightly less than the temperature on the Earth?

....

e) Which planet is nearest to the Earth?

....

f) Which planet is nearest to Saturn?

....

g) What relationship can you see between the time it takes a planet to orbit the Sun once, and its distance from the Sun?

....

h) Which planet has the lowest surface temperature?

....

i) Give one reason why this planet is so cold.

....

j) How many planets in our Solar System have a mass which is less than that of the Earth?

....

k) Which planet takes almost twice as long to orbit the Sun than Uranus?

....

Score   /11

How well did you do?   ✗ 1–7 Try again   8–12 Getting there   13–19 Good work   20–27 Excellent! ✓

The Solar System 2

The motions of all objects in our Solar System are controlled by gravitational forces.

A Choose just one answer, a, b, c or d.

1 What forces hold the Solar System together?
(1 mark)
a) frictional   b) magnetic
c) gravitational   d) electrical

2 Which of the following is true for comets?
(1 mark)
a) They orbit planets.
b) They are mainly found between Mars and Jupiter.
c) They are large rock-like pieces of ice.
d) They travel between star systems.

3 What is an elliptical orbit? (1 mark)
a) one that looks like a slightly squashed circle
b) one that is circular
c) one that goes clockwise
d) one that is bigger than the Sun

4 If the Moon passes between the Sun and the Earth it may cause (1 mark)
a) a fall of meteorites
b) a lunar eclipse
c) a solar eclipse
d) Sun spots

5 How strong, approximately, is gravity on the Moon compared with that on the Earth?
(1 mark)
a) one sixth
b) 6 times greater
c) the same
d) one tenth

Score /5

B Answer all parts of all questions.

1 Rearrange the letters of the words in the list below, then write a sentence to explain what the word means.
(10 marks)

a) etcmo ....
b) tanple ....
c) arst ....
d) dasitero ....
e) nsu ....
f) onmo ....
g) solar eclipse ....
h) lunar eclipse ....
i) gravitational forces ....
j) lunar month ....

120

C These are SATs-style questions. Answer all parts of the questions.

1 The diagram below shows the positions of the Sun, Moon and Earth during a solar eclipse.

solar eclipse

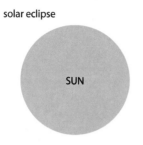

SUN

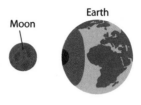

Moon

Earth

Not to scale

a) Using a ruler, draw four rays of light to show how a solar eclipse takes place. (4 marks)

b) Why in the very centre of the shadow do we see a total eclipse? (1 mark)

....

c) In the space below draw a diagram to show the positions of the Sun, Earth and Moon during a lunar eclipse. (2 marks)

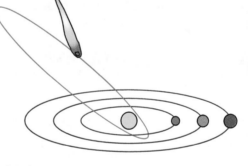

2 The diagram opposite shows a comet orbiting the Sun.

a) What forces keep the comet in orbit around the Sun? (1 mark)

....

b) When are these forces largest? (1 mark)

....

c) Where in the orbit of a comet is it travelling fastest? (1 mark)

....

d) From what is a comet's tail made? (1 mark)

....

Score   /11

How well did you do?   ✗ 1–7 **Try again**   8–12 **Getting there**   13–19 **Good work**   20–26 **Excellent!** ✓

SATs exam practice questions

1 The labelled diagram below shows a typical animal cell.   (3 marks)

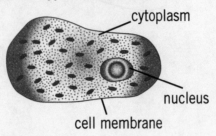

cytoplasm

nucleus

cell membrane

Use the labels to fill in the table below.

Function	Part
controls all the cell's activities	nucleus
where chemical reactions take place	cytoplasm
controls what passes in and out of the cell	cell membrane

2 a) A piece of copper metal is heated until it melts. The change of state that takes
place is from ....Solid.... to ...liquid...   (2 marks)

b) 5 g of copper was heated until it melted. What was the mass of the melted copper?
   ....5........... g   (1 mark)

3 The table below shows some energy changes. Fill in the gaps. The first one has been
done for you.   (7 marks)

Energy in	Energy changer	Energy out
electrical	light bulb	heat and light
electrical	radio	sound
electrical	microwave	heat
chemical		heat and light
wind	wind turbine	electrical
light	solar panels	electrical

4 Metals are used to make many objects. Draw a line to connect each metal to its use and
to the property of that metal which makes it suitable for that particular use.   (6 marks)

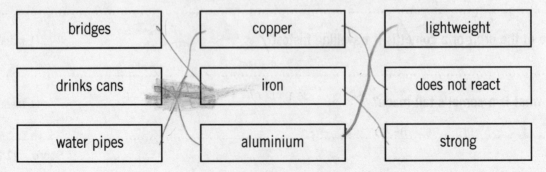

bridges	copper	lightweight
drinks cans	iron	does not react
water pipes	aluminium	strong

5 **a)** Using the words below, label the diagram of the breathing system. *(6 marks)*

trachea   alveoli   bronchioles   bronchi   diaphragm   intercostal muscles

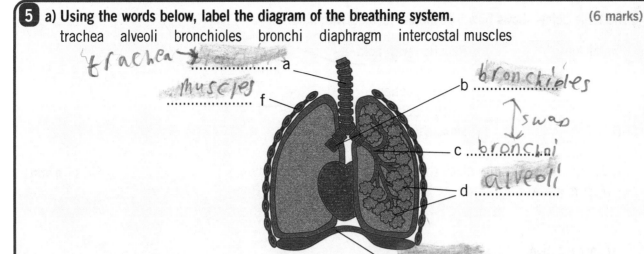

a — trachea ~~trachea~~
f — muscles
b — bronchioles
c — bronchoi / swap → bronchial
d — alveoli

b) Which of the two labelled parts work together to help us breathe in and out? *(2 marks)*

d and e

c) What is the name of the organ in the diagram that lies between the lungs? *(1 mark)*

heart

6 The diagram opposite shows the colour triangle.

The table below shows what happens when different coloured lights overlap. Use the colour triangle to fill in the gaps in the table below. *(6 marks)*

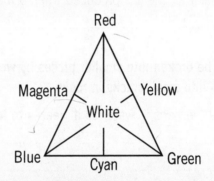

Colour A	Colour B	Colour A + Colour B
red	green	yellow
red	blue	magenta
blue	green	cyan
blue	yellow	white
green	magenta	white
cyan	red	white

7 The diagrams below show an alveolus from a healthy person and an alveolus from a person suffering from emphysema. *(2 marks)*

alveolus (air sac)

healthy person

person suffering from emphysema

Explain using the diagram how the damaged alveolus makes breathing difficult.

8 The table below shows how four metals reacted with acid.

Metal	Reaction with acid
A	no reaction
B	violent reaction
C	quick reaction
D	slow reaction

a) Use the table above to place the metals in order of reactivity.   (4 marks)

Most reactive ....*B*............

............*C*............

............*D*............

Least reactive ....*A*............

b) Use the table to suggest which of the metals could be gold.   (1 mark)

A

c) Use the table to suggest which of the metals could be potassium.   (1 mark)

B

d) What is the name of the gas produced when a metal reacts with acid?   (1 mark)

carbon dioxide

9 Large rocks can be broken into smaller pieces by weathering. One type of weathering involves water. The water enters into small cracks in rocks.

a) Describe what happens to water as it freezes to form ice.   (1 mark)

the small cracks give in and breack the rock

b) Explain how this can cause a rock to be weathered.   (1 mark)

It will ~~breack~~ breack the rock

10 The following is a food chain from a woodland.

oak leaves ⟹ woodlouse ⟹ blackbird

a) Which animal is a herbivore?

woodlouse   (1 mark)

b) Which animal is a carnivore?

black bird   (1 mark)

c) There were 20 oak leaves, 10 woodlice and 5 blackbirds in this food chain. Draw a pyramid of numbers to represent this information.   (2 marks)

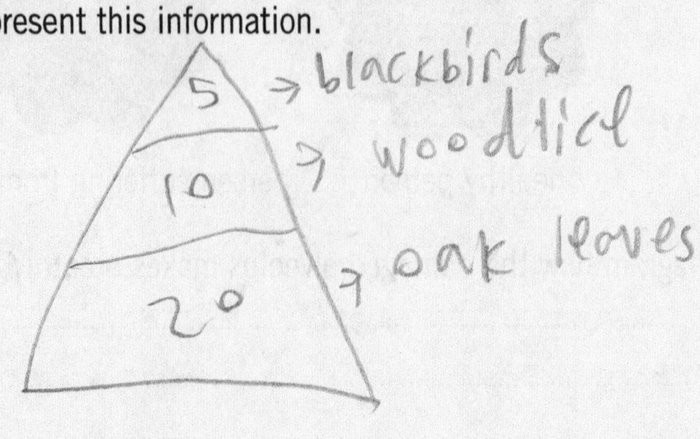

5 → blackbirds
10 → woodlice
20 → oak leaves

11 Kevin has a new blue pen. He uses chromatography to investigate the ink in his new pen. His experiment is shown below.

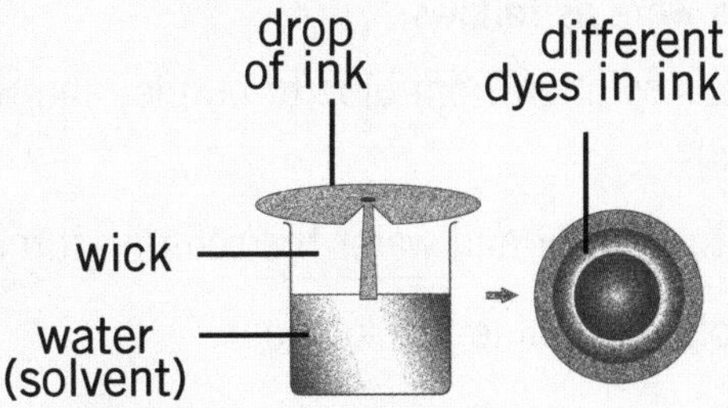

drop of ink

different dyes in ink

wick

water (solvent)

a) Why did Kevin use filter paper in his experiment? **(1 mark)**

....

....

b) Why did Kevin draw a line across the bottom of his chromatogram using a pencil and not a pen? **(1 mark)**

..........*so it wont mix*...

c) How could Kevin tell how many different coloured substances were present in the ink of his new pen? **(1 mark)**

.........*count them*...

....

12 The table below shows what happens when different coloured lights try to pass through a coloured filter. Use the colour triangle in Q6 to fill in the gaps. **(5 marks)**

Colour of light	Colour of filter	Colour of light that passes through filter
white	red	*red*
blue	red	*white*
yellow	red	*red*
magenta	blue	*blue*
green	cyan	*blue*

13 Alistair is given a pile of objects made from steel, copper and wood.

a) Suggest one way in which Alistair could separate the steel objects from those made of copper and wood.

.........*magnet*.. **(1 mark)**

b) Suggest one way in which Alistair could separate the copper objects from those made of wood.

.... **(1 mark)**

c) Alistair builds an electrical circuit similar to that shown below. Explain how he could use this circuit to discover which of the three materials in his pile are conductors and which are insulators. **(4 marks)**

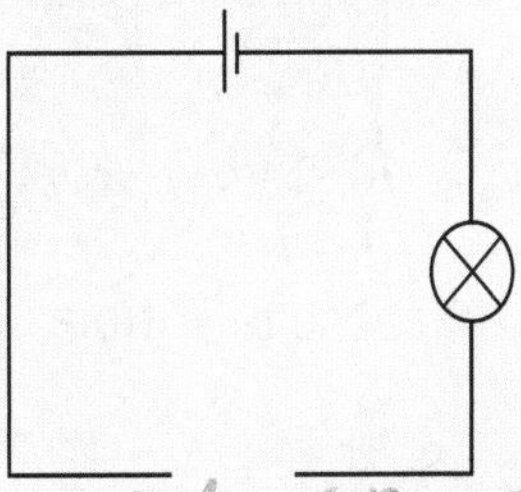

.........*to test them out on the wires to see which type they are (conductors and insulators)*...

....

14 a) **Shelley and Peter carried out some food tests on a cheese sandwich to see what nutrients it contained. The results were as follows:** (4 marks)

cheese – changed Biuret's solution from blue to purple, and when tested with ethanol and water the solution turned cloudy

butter – when tested with ethanol and water the solution turned cloudy

bread – turned iodine solution a blue-black colour

From these results what nutrients did they contain? Put a tick in the correct column.

	Protein	Fat	Starch
cheese	✓		
butter		✓	
bread			✓

(4 marks)

b) Adding Benedict's solution and heating a food sample is the test for glucose. The solution is a blue colour to begin with. What colour does it change to if glucose is present? (1 mark)

....

15 Sue placed a small piece of magnesium metal into some blue copper sulphate solution. Complete the equation below to show the reaction in Sue's experiment.

a) Magnesium + copper sulphate → *MGiSWPhate* + *copper* (2 marks)

b) Sue noticed that a brown substance now coated the magnesium metal. What was the brown substance?

........*rust*... (1 mark)

16 The diagram below shows a synovial joint in the body.

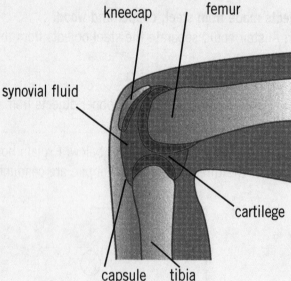

hinge joint (e.g. knee, elbow, wrist)

kneecap   femur

synovial fluid

cartilege

capsule   tibia

a) What is the function of the synovial fluid? (1 mark)

......*to allow more movement*...

b) What is the function of cartilage? (1 mark)

......*to protect things*..

17 a) The diagram below is a leaf, the organ of photosynthesis.

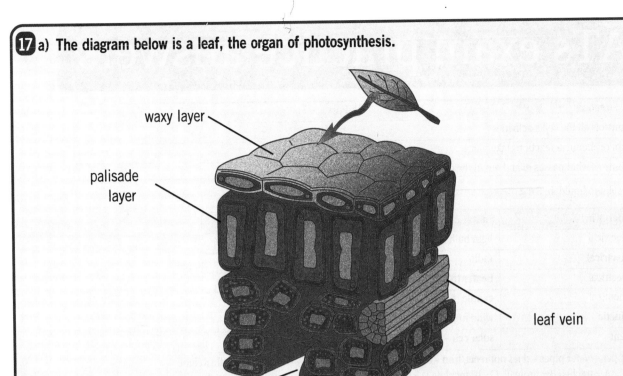

waxy layer

palisade layer

leaf vein

stoma

Look at the labelled parts and decide which part matches which function by drawing 4 lines.

stoma   prevents the leaf from losing too much water

waxy layer   the place where most photosynthesis takes place

palisade layer   transports water and minerals to the leaf

leaf vein   where carbon dioxide enters the leaf   **(4 marks)**

b) **What else apart from water and carbon dioxide does a leaf need to be able to photosynthesise?**   **(2 marks)**

Sun light

     (2 marks)

18 **Calcium carbonate is the main compound in the rock limestone.**   **(2 marks)**
When calcium carbonate is heated fiercely it decomposes to produce the gas carbon dioxide and a solid called calcium oxide.
Write a word equation to show this reaction.

....

....

19 **Katy and Richard are standing barefoot in their house. Katy is standing on ceramic tiles.**
Her feet feel cold. Richard is standing on a carpet. His feet feel warm. Explain why Katy's feet
feel cold and Richard's feet feel warm.   **(4 marks)**

the coorple is a conducer of heat and the tiles are not

....

....

1.

Function	Part
controls all the cell's activities	**nucleus**
where chemical reactions take place	**cytoplasm**
controls what passes in and out of the cell	**cell membrane**

2 a) solid to liquid b) 5.0 g

3.

Energy in	Energy changer	Energy out
electrical	light bulb	heat and light
electrical	radio	**sound**
electrical	**heater (resistor)**	heat
chemical	**candle (fire)**	heat and light
kinetic	wind turbine	**electrical**
light	**solar cell**	electrical

4 copper – water pipes – does not react/iron – bridges – strong/aluminium – drinks cans – lightweight

5 a)   A = trachea B = bronchi C = bronchiole D = alveoli E = diaphragm F = intercostal muscle
   b) diaphragm and intercostal muscles c) the heart

6.

Colour A	Colour B	Colour A + Colour B
red	green	**yellow**
red	blue	**magenta**
blue	green	**cyan**
blue	yellow	**white**
green	magenta	**white**
cyan	red	**white**

7 The surface area of the damaged alveoli is reduced (1 mark), which makes gas exchange difficult or makes it more difficult for oxygen to get to the cells and carbon dioxide to be removed (1 mark)

8 a) B, C, D, A   b) A   c) B   d) hydrogen

9 a) it expands   b) the ice expands and forces the existing crack further apart

10 a) woodlouse   b) blackbird
    c) 1 mark for a pyramid drawn in proportion (i.e. larger at the bottom and narrowing up to the third layer, representing the numbers 20 at the bottom then 10 then 5 at the top), 1 mark for labelling the layers oak leaves, woodlice and blackbird

11 a) filter paper is porous   b) pencil is insoluble/pen is soluble
    c) Kevin should count the number of different coloured inks that develop on his chromatogram

12.

Colour of light	Colour of filter	Colour of light that passes through filter
white	red	**red**
blue	red	**none**
yellow	red	**red**
magenta	blue	**blue**
green	cyan	**green**

13 a) he could use a magnet which would attract just the pieces of steel
    b) he could put them into a bowl of water; the wooden pieces will float and the copper pieces will sink
    c) with the circuit incomplete the bulb does not light (1), if a conductor is placed across the gap the circuit is complete (1) and the bulb will glow (1), if an insulator is placed across the gap the bulb will not glow (1)

14 a) cheese contains protein and fat, butter contains fat, bread contains starch b) orange

15 a) magnesium sulphate + copper b) copper

16 a) the synovial fluid reduces friction/prevents the bones sliding and grinding against each other and causing damage
    b) cartilage acts as a shock absorber/protects the bones from knocking together and wearing away.

17 a) stoma   where carbon dioxide enters the leaf
       waxy layer   prevents the leaf from losing too much water
       palisade layer   the place where most photosynthesis takes place
       leaf vein   transports water and minerals to the leaf
    b) chlorophyll and sunlight

18 calcium carbonate → calcium oxide + carbon dioxide

19 the carpet is a very poor conductor of heat (1), it prevents heat loss from Richard's feet so they feel warm (1), the ceramic tiles are better conductors (1), heat escapes more quickly from Katy's feet and so they feel colder than Richard's (1)